MULTIPLE-CHOICE & FREE-RESPONSE QUESTIONS IN PREPARATION FOR THE AP CALCULUS (BC) EXAMINATION

(NINTH EDITION)

David Lederman

With the assistance of:

Lin McMullin

and

Bob Byrne

 **D&S MARKETING SYSTEMS, INC.**
1205 38th Street Brooklyn, NY 11218

www.dsmarketing.com

ISBN # : 978-1-934780-44-2 / 1-934780-44-8

PREFACE

I am pleased to offer you the 9th edition of MULTIPLE-CHOICE & FREE-RESPONSE QUESTIONS IN PREPARATION FOR THE AP CALCULUS (BC) EXAMINATION.

This book has been prepared with one purpose in mind: to help you prepare for the Advanced Placement Calculus BC Examination. It should be made clear that you will have to respond to both multiple-choice and free-response questions on the examination. Some parts of the examination do not allow the use of graphing calculators and other parts have questions which are calculator-dependent.

➢ The 9th edition consists of six sample examinations, each with forty-five multiple-choice questions and six free-response questions.

- Section I Part A consists of 30 multiple-choice questions in which the use of calculators is not allowed.
- Section I Part B consists of 15 multiple-choice questions designed with graphing calculators in mind, and contains some questions for which this technology is required.
- Section II Part A consists of two free-response questions and contains some questions or parts of questions for which a graphing calculator is required.
- Section II Part B consists of four free-response questions for which you may not use your calculator.

You now have an opportunity to take a series of six examinations under conditions that simulate those in an actual test administration.

➢ Workspace for each question has been provided for you.
➢ As indicated on the actual AP Calculus BC examination you should allow yourself and follow these test-taking time limits.
- Section I Part A — 60 minutes
- Section I Part B — 45 minutes
- Section II Part A — 30 minutes
- Section II Part B — 60 minutes
➢ Formulas and Theorems for Reference are provided at the end of the book, however this information is not provided on an actual Calculus BC examination.

I believe that by completing all six sample examinations:
➢ you will be able to identify your strengths and weaknesses in your understanding of Calculus;
➢ you will be able to better prepare a study plan for the Calculus BC examination;
➢ you will be able to approach the AP Calculus BC Examination with increased confidence.

Any errors found in this book are solely the responsibility of the author.

All communications concerning this book should be addressed to:

D & S Marketing Systems, Inc.
1205 38th Street
Brooklyn, NY 11218
www.dsmarketing.com

ACKNOWLEDGMENTS

The author wishes to thank the following individuals for their contributions and assistance in the publication of this book.

To Bob Byrne of St. Thomas Aquinas HS (Ft. Lauderdale, FL) for sharing ideas and making valuable suggestions in the revision and editing of this 9th edition.

To Lin McMullin for his Student Survival Guide essay, as well as contributing many graphing, calculator, and free-response questions which have been included in this edition.

To Tammi Pruzansky of D&S Marketing Systems, Inc., for preparing the graphs and typesetting the entire manuscript of this 9th edition.

A special debt of gratitude is due to my wife, Sara Lederman, for her many years of encouragement and patience and to whom I wish to dedicate this book in her loving memory.

TABLE OF CONTENTS

The AP Calculus Exam
How, not only to Survive, but to Prevail...

By Lin McMullin

The AP Calculus exam is the cumulation of all of the years you've spent in high school studying mathematics. It's all led up to this. The calculus you study in the last year completes the prior years of preparation. If you are reading this at the beginning of the year keep these things in mind as you go through the year. If you are reading this only a few weeks before the test think back and see how these things fit together.

Everything in calculus, and mathematics in general, is best understood verbally, numerically, analytically (that is, through the use of equations and symbols) and graphically. Look at everything from these four perspectives. Look at the relationships among them — how the same idea shows up in words, in equations, in numbers and in graphs.

For example: numerically a linear function is one which when written as a table of values, regular changes in the x-values produce regular changes in the y-values. Graphically a linear function has a graph that is a straight line. Analytically it is one whose equation can be written as $y = mx + b$. And the three ways are interrelated. The ratio of the changes in the table is the number m in the equation; the graph can be drawn using the number m by going up and over from one point to the next. The idea of the slope as "rise over run" expresses this verbally. Everything in mathematics and in the calculus works that way.

Learn the concepts — the exam emphasizes concepts.

Learn the procedures and formulas — even though the concepts are more important than the computations you still have to do the computations. Like it or not, learn to do the algebra, the arithmetic and the graphs.

Learn to be methodical — work neatly and carefully all year.

i

Think about what you are doing. Watch yourself work. It is natural to concentrate on the material you know and can do, but you need to concentrate on the things you do not (yet) know how to do. You can learn much from your mistakes. Look at a wrong answer as a green light to go in a different direction until you've reached the right answer.

Reviewing for the Exam

In the few weeks before the AP Exam you will need to review what you have studied, firm up what you have learned, work on your areas of weakness, and, yes, memorize some formulas. You also need to prepare for the exam itself by learning what kinds of questions will be asked and how to best answer them. Specifically

- Understand the format of the exams. (See below). Know how your knowledge will be tested.
- STUDY WHAT YOU DO NOT KNOW. That may seem obvious but many people enjoy getting the right answers so much that they only review the stuff they know. The time to concentrate on what you know is when you are taking the test.
- Practice writing free-response answers. The College Board publishes copies of student answers from past years. If your teacher has some of these, look at them and learn what is expected and what is not needed.
- Plan your review carefully. Don't try to cram the weekend before the exam. The day before the test: relax, get psyched, and get a good night's sleep. On the day of the test eat a good breakfast. The test is grueling, even though you're up for it. Bring a snack for the brief break between the multiple-chose and free-response sections.

Graphing Calculators

The reason calculators are so important in learning mathematics is that they allow you do the graphical and numerical work easily, quickly and accurately. You should use your calculator all year, on homework, tests and when studying. Learn how to use it efficiently. Learn its strengths and weaknesses.

You may use your calculator any way you wish. There are four types of things you must know how to do. They are

- Plot the graph of a function within an arbitrary viewing window,
- Find the zeros of functions (solve equations numerically). One way to do this is to graph both sides of the equation and find the point(s) of intersection.

- Numerically calculate the value of the derivative of a function at a point, and
- Numerically calculate the value of a definite integral.

You may have programs in your calculator; but you will not be asked to use them. The questions on the exam are designed so that someone with a program, or a more expensive calculator, or a computer algebra system, has no advantage over someone who does not. This includes many of the built-in programs.

Be sure your graphing calculator is set in Radian mode.

Numerical answers may be left unsimplified and in terms of π, e, etc. There is no reason to change an answer to a decimal if you don't have to. (Why take the chance on pushing the wrong button?)

Install fresh batteries before the exam.

The Format of the Exams

There are two parts to the AP exams: a multiple-choice section and a free-response section. The number of questions and timing may change slightly from year to year. Be sure you check the current College Board publications for your exam.

Both sections count equally towards your final grade. Both sections cover the full range of topics. It is natural to expect that different classes will cover some topics in greater detail than others; the exam will evaluate your knowledge of the calculus. It is not necessary to answer all the questions to get a good score. In fact the exam is made so that the average score will be about 50%; this is usually a score of three.

The Current AP Calculus Exam format is

Section I Part A (60 minutes) 30 multiple-choice questions for which you may not use a calculator.

Section I Part B (45 minutes) 15 multiple-choice questions. You may use your calculator on this section. Some of these questions require the use of a graphing calculator others do not.

Section II Part A (30 minutes) Two Free-Response questions. In this section you will find longer questions with several related parts. You will need your calculator for some parts (but not all parts) of questions in this section. You are required to show your work in this section. You may continue work on this section without a calculator after you start part B.

Section II Part B (60 minutes) Four Free-Response questions. You may not use your calculator on this section. In this section you will find longer questions with several related parts. You are required to show your work in this section. You may use part of this time to work on Section II, Part A without a calculator

Sections I and II count equally towards your final score.

Multiple-Choice Questions

Read each question carefully and look at the answer choices. Do the ones you are sure of. Don't struggle over one that isn't working out. Remember your time is limited and you do not need to answer all of the questions. There is no longer a penalty for guessing; nevertheless, don't guess blindly. Try to eliminate one or more of the choices before guessing.

Do not waste time on questions you are struggling with. A good procedure is to do all the "easy" questions, the ones you are sure of, first. Then go back and do the more difficult ones you think you can do, and then, if there is time, try the ones you are not sure you can do. Do not leave any question unanswered.

Be sure to bubble your answer in the correct space on the answer sheet.

Types of Multiple-Choice Questions

- One type of question may ask for a computation (a limit, a derivative, a definite or indefinite integral) and give four possible answers: be aware that answers that result from predictable mistakes are among the choices — work carefully, just because your answer is there doesn't mean it's correct.
- Another type may ask you only to set up a problem: looking at the answer choices may keep you from doing too much work.
- Some questions ask you to choose the one true or one false statement from a list of four statements: be sure you know if you are looking for a true or a false statement.
- Another type of question asks which of three statements is true (or false): the answer may be any one or some combination of the statements.
- Another type may ask you to choose the correct table or graph from among four choices.

Free-response Questions

The general directions for Section II require you to show your work and indicate the methods you use to arrive at your answers. In addition, parts of questions may say, "Justify your answer" or "Explain your reasoning" or "Show the analysis that leads to your conclusion." Your answers will be read by calculus teachers who will judge your work. It is important that you clearly show how you arrived at your answer. Answers without supporting work may lose points even if the final answer is correct.

The questions are designed to show the breadth and depth of your knowledge. There are some common types of questions that are asked. There will also be questions asked in new and original ways.

Some things to keep in mind about free-response questions:

- Don't write a long essay: it's not necessary. Do show the work that you do, so that the reader will understand you. You may use common terms and names like "the first derivative test." You do not need to name theorems. Explain in words and symbols what you see in the given information (the graph or table) that leads you to your conclusion; relate your reasoning to the given information or graph.

- Your justifications and explanations must be in word and symbols. Number lines are an excellent way to organize the information, but they do not count as justifications. Readers are forbidden to even look at number line justifications.

- The free-response section of the exam rarely requires long complicated computation; if you find yourself doing a long complicated computation you've probably gone wrong somewhere and should start over.

- Do not explain how to do the problem you cannot do. A general explanation without work will receive no credit. You must do the problem you are given.

- *Avoid simplifying numerical answers.* If you get $1 + 1$ for your answer, leave it that way. Answers may be left unsimplified as fractions, radicals, powers of e, in terms of π etc. Do not take a chance of pushing the wrong button once you have an acceptable answer. If you do arithmetic it must be done correctly. Every year students find the correct answer, simplify it or change it to a decimal incorrectly and lose a point. Decimal answers (for example a definite integral on a calculator) are acceptable even if an exact answer is possible.

- If you make a mistake cross it out. Crossed out work is not read or graded. If you leave wrong work on your paper (not crossed out) it will be read and may affect your score.

- If you work the problem two different ways, choose the best one and put an X through the other. If both are left, they will both be scored and the scores will be averaged. This can lower your score even if one solution is perfect.

- Standard notation must be used. Don't use calculator notation. (For example: $\texttt{fnInt(x}^2\texttt{,x,0,2)}$ is not acceptable, use the standard $\int_0^2 x^2 dx$.

- Answers without work may not receive full credit. Don't do work on a calculator without indicating what you are doing. For example if you are evaluating a definite integral write the integral on your paper and put the calculator answer next to it; you do not need to show the work in between (the antiderivative).

- Different calculators have different built-in utilities (for example the ability to find points of inflection, or maximum values of a function). You may have programs in your calculator to do things such as the the left or right Riemann sum (LRAM, RRAM) or the Trapezoidal approximation. However, if you use such a built-in utility or a special program to do something other than the four things listed previously, you must show on your paper the complete set-up (the terms of the Riemann sum approximation or the Trapezoidal approximation, the computation, analysis of the second derivative required to find a point of inflection, etc.). Only the four things listed above may be done without further explanation.

- Don't put things where they are not needed. Work must be shown on the part of the answer booklet where it is used. For example, if you need a derivative in part (b) of a question and you have it in part (a) where it is not needed, you will not get credit for finding the derivative (in either part). Either copy it in part (b) or draw an arrow over to where you wrote it. You must show you know where you need the derivative as well as your ability to find it. Likewise, do not put work on the graph or drawing. It may not be read unless you specifically refer to it in the part of the answer booklet where you used it.

- Finally the parts of a free-response question are related to each other. This can help you in two ways:
  - Sometimes each part may be answered without reference to the other parts. Read and try of all the parts: if you cannot do part (a) maybe you can do part (b). Perhaps doing part (b) will give you a hint on how to do part (a).

- Other times the one part will lead to the next: this is done to help you find your way through the problem. Keep in mind that this may be the case and work your way from part (a) to part (b) to part (c) even if you're not sure where the problem is heading.

■ Try all of the free-response questions. They are written so that the first parts are easier in order to help you get started. Even if you don't get the entire problem, earning some points are better than earning no points.

Common Free-Response Mistakes

■ Algebra and arithmetic mistakes.

■ Missing limits of integration.

■ Not considering the end points of an interval (for example, when looking for the absolute maximum value of a function).

■ Giving answers from points outside the given interval.

■ Not giving both coordinates of a point when required.

■ Giving both coordinates when only one is asked for; remember "value of a function" means the y-value and "maximum value of a function" means the absolute maximum y-value.

■ Not having your calculator in radian mode.

■ Not answering the question that was asked even though all the work is correct. If it is a yes or no question, say "yes" or "no."

■ Ignoring units of measure, if they are specifically asked for.

■ Family of function problems: Questions that start with a phrase like, "This question deals with functions defined by $f(x) = 1 + b \sin(x)$ where b is a positive constant..." are meant to be done in general, *not* for a specific value of b. Even if you get the correct answer using a specific value of b, you may lose points. The reason is that, because you used a particular value, you have no way to be sure that your answers are true for all values of b.

■ Curve Fitting: There will be a function given as a graph or a table of values with no equation. You are being asked to demonstrate that you can work from the graphical or numerical data. The questions that follow can be answered *without* an equation. You may have learned to approximate functions using various curve fitting (regression) operations built into your calculator. *This should be avoided.* While this is a perfectly good approach in the real world, you may lose points because you are not working with the function you were given (only an approximation of it), and this is not one of the four allowed calculator operations. Do not curve fit.

- Using a built-in calculator utility or a program without showing all the work and justification for what you are doing. You may do only the four things mentioned above without further explanation.

A Word about Three-Decimal Place Accuracy

Some answers, the evaluation of definite integrals is an example, must be written as decimals because they are found using a graphing calculator. These answers, and other answers that you choose to change to decimals, must be correct to three places past the decimal point. This means that the answer may be rounded to three decimal places, truncated after the third decimal place or left with more than three decimal places as long as the first three are correct. An answer of π, which should be left as π, may be given as $3.1415926535898\ldots$, 3.142, 3.141, 3.1416785 or even 3.142768. If the number ends in zeros, they may be omitted; thus 17.320 may be given as 17.32 and 56.000 may be given as 56.

Too often, students may choose to give decimal answers when they are not required. Once a free-response answer is entirely in terms of numbers there is no need to change the number to a decimal. For example, 2012 BC 1(a) does *not* require a decimal answer: $\frac{67.9 - 61.8}{6}$ is sufficient. If the decimal is correct (to three decimal places) then you will receive the credit. However, if you change a correct answer to an incorrect decimal (including one with too few decimals) then you will lose credit. The moral is: avoid arithmetic, avoid decimals; give them only if you cannot give anything else.

Rounding too soon is another common mistake made by students. Computations should be done with more decimal places than is required in the final answer. Learn how to store the intermediate values in your calculator and recall them when you need them in a computation. If premature rounding affects the three decimal place accuracy of the final answer, you will not be given the answer point. However, a rounded answer used in the next part of a problem will not be held against you.

Good Luck!

SAMPLE EXAMINATION I
SECTION I PART A

NO CALCULATOR IS ALLOWED IN THIS SECTION.

Directions: Solve each of the following problems, using the available space for scratch work. After examining the form of the choices, decide which is the best of the choices given. Do not spend too much time on any one problem.

In this exam:

(1) Unless otherwise specified, the domain of a function f is assumed to be the set of all real numbers x for which $f(x)$ is a real number.

(2) The inverse of a trigonometric function f may be indicated using the inverse function notation f^{-1} or with the prefix "arc" (e.g., $\sin^{-1}x = \arcsin x$)

1. $f(x) = \begin{cases} x^2 + 5, & x < -2 \\ 2 - 4x, & x \geq -2 \end{cases}$

Let f be the function defined above. The value of $f'(-2)$ is

(A) -2 (B) -4 (C) 4 (D) nonexistent

$2 - 4x = -4$

Answer

2. The graph of $y = 3x^2 - x^3$ has a relative maximum at

(A) $(0,0)$ only

(B) $(1,2)$ only

(C) $(2,4)$ only

(D) $(4,-16)$ only

$3x^2(2-x)$

$x = 0, 1,$

$6x - 3x^2 = 0 \quad 3x(2-x)$

$x = 0, 2$

Answer

3. A particle moves in the xy-plane so that its velocity vector at time t is $v(t) = \langle t^2, \sin(\pi t) \rangle$ and the particle's position vector at time $t = 0$ is $\langle 1, 0 \rangle$. What is the position vector of the particle when $t = 3$?

   (A) $\left\langle 9, \dfrac{1}{\pi} \right\rangle$ (B) $\left\langle 10, \dfrac{2}{\pi} \right\rangle$ (C) $\langle 10, 2\pi \rangle$ (D) $\langle 10, 2 \rangle$

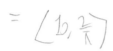

Answer

[ ]

4. For what values of x does the curve $y^2 - x^3 - 15x^2 = 4$ have horizontal tangent lines?

   (A) $x = 0$ only

   (B) $x = 10$ only

   (C) $x = -10$ and $x = 0$ only

   (D) $x = -10$, $x = 0$, and $x = 10$

Answer

[ ]

5. What is the radius of convergence for the power series $\sum_{n=0}^{\infty}(3x-5)^n$?

(A) $\frac{1}{3}$ (B) $\frac{2}{3}$ (C) 1   (D) $\frac{5}{3}$

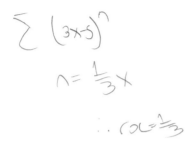

$$\sum (3x-5)^n$$

$$n = \frac{1}{3}x$$

$$\therefore x = \frac{1}{3}$$

Answer

6. $\lim\limits_{x \to 0} \dfrac{4x^2 + \sin(x)}{2x^2 - x} =$

(A) 2   (B) 1   (C) 0   (D) −1

$$\frac{0+0}{0-0}$$

$$= \frac{8x + \cos(x)}{4x - 1} = -1$$

Answer

7. If $f(x) = \sqrt{2 - 4\sin x}$, then $f'(\pi) =$

(A) $-\sqrt{2}$ (B) 0   (C) $\dfrac{\sqrt{2}}{2}$ (D) $\sqrt{2}$

$(2-4\sin x)^{1/2}$

$\dfrac{1}{2}(2-4\sin x)^{-1/2}$

$\dfrac{1}{2\sqrt{2-4\sin x}} = \dfrac{1}{2\sqrt{2-0}} = \dfrac{1}{2\sqrt{2}}$

Answer

8. $\displaystyle\int_{2}^{4}\left[\dfrac{d}{dt}(3t^2 + 2t - 1)\right] dt =$

(A) 12   (B) 40   (C) 46   (D) 55

$\left. 3t^2 + 2t - 1 \right|_{2}^{4}$

$= 86 - 46$

Answer

9. Let a_n, b_n, and c_n be sequences of positive numbers such that for all positive integers n, $a_n \leq b_n \leq c_n$. If $\displaystyle\sum_{n=1}^{\infty} b_n$ converges, then which of the following statements must be true?

$\quad$ I. $\displaystyle\sum_{n=1}^{\infty} a_n$ converges

$\quad$ II. $\displaystyle\sum_{n=1}^{\infty} c_n$ converges

$\quad$ III. $\displaystyle\sum_{n=1}^{\infty} (a_n + b_n)$ converges

(A) II only

(B) III only

(C) I and III only

(D) I, II, and III

Answer

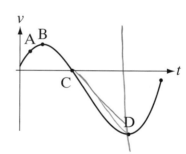

10. For an object moving along a straight line, the graph above represents the velocity of the moving object as a function of time. At which of the marked points is the speed the greatest?

(A) A $\qquad$ (B) B $\qquad$ (C) C $\qquad$ (D) D

Answer

11. $\lim_{n \to \infty} \sum_{k=1}^{n} \left[2 + \frac{3}{n}k \right]^2 \left(\frac{3}{n} \right) =$

    (A)   13   (B) $\frac{125}{3}$ (C)   39   (D)   125

$$\left[2 + \frac{3}{n}k \right]^2 \left(\frac{3}{n} \right) = 13 \left(\frac{3}{1} \right) = \boxed{39}$$

Answer

12. $\int \frac{1}{\sqrt{4 - x^2}} \, dx =$

    (A) $\sin^{-1} \left(\frac{x}{2} \right) + C$

    (B) $2 \sqrt{4 - x^2} + C$

    (C) $\sqrt{4 - x^2} + C$

    (D) $\frac{1}{2} \sin^{-1} \left(\frac{x}{2} \right) + C$

$$\frac{1}{\sqrt{1 - x^2}} = \sin^{-1}(\text{...} x)$$
$$= \sin^{-1} \left(\frac{x}{2} \right)$$

Answer

13. If the graph of $f(x) = 2x^2 + \dfrac{k}{x}$ has a point of inflection at $x = -1$, then the value of k is

(A) −2   (B) −1   (C) 1   (D) 2

kx^{-2}

$4x \cdot \cancel{0} - k\cancel{0}$ over x^2

$4 - \dfrac{k}{x}$

$-4 + \dfrac{k}{x} = 0$

$\dfrac{4}{2} = k$

$k = 2$

Answer

14. If $f(x) = \cos^{-1}(2x)$, then $f'(x) =$

(A) $\dfrac{-2}{\sqrt{1 + 4x^2}}$

(B) $\dfrac{-2}{\sqrt{1 - 4x^2}}$

(C) $\dfrac{2}{\sqrt{1 - 4x^2}}$

(D) $\dfrac{2}{\sqrt{1 + 4x^2}}$

Answer

15. Which of the following is an equation of the line tangent to the curve with parametric equations $x = 3e^{-t}$, $y = 6e^t$ at the point where $t = 0$?

(A) $2x + y - 12 = 0$

$3e^{-t} = 6e^{-t}$

(B) $2x - y + 12 = 0$

(C) $x - 2y + 9 = 0$

$2x = -y + 12$

(D) $2x - y = 0$

$2x + y - 12 = 0$

Answer

16. $\int \dfrac{dx}{2x^2 + 3x + 1} =$

(A) $2 \ln \left| \dfrac{2x+1}{x+1} \right| + C$

(B) $\ln \left| \dfrac{(2x+1)^2}{x+1} \right| + C$

(C) $\ln \left| \dfrac{2x+1}{x+1} \right| + C$

(D) $\ln \left| \dfrac{x+1}{2x+1} \right| + C$

Answer

17. If $x = 2 \sin t$ and $y = \cos^2 t$, then $\dfrac{d^2 y}{dx^2}$ at $t = \pi$ equals

(A) -1 (B) $-\dfrac{1}{2}$ (C) 0 (D) 1

Answer

18. The rate of change of the surface area of a cube, A, with respect to time, t, is directly proportional to the square root of one-sixth of the surface area. If at $t = 0$ the surface area of the cube is 24 and the rate of change of the surface area is 8, how fast is the surface area changing when the side length of the cube is 4 ?

(A) 16 (B) 24 (C) 32 (D) 48

Answer

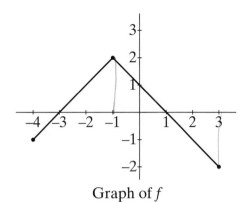

Graph of f

19. The graph of a piecewise linear function f is shown above. If $g(x) = \int_{-1}^{x} f(t)\,dt$, which of the following is true?

(A) $g(-4) = g(-1)$

(B) $g(-3) = g(3)$

(C) $g(-1) = g(3)$

(D) $g(0) = g(-4)$

Answer

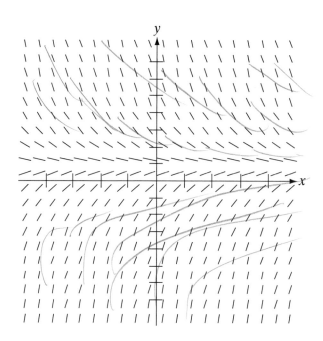

20. Shown above is the slope field for which of the following differential equations?

(A) $\dfrac{dy}{dx} = x - y$

(B) $\dfrac{dy}{dx} = -\dfrac{x}{y}$

(C) $\dfrac{dy}{dx} = 1 + y^2$

(D) $\dfrac{dy}{dx} = 1 - y$

$-y+1$

Answer

21. The power series $1 + 2x + 4x^2 + 8x^3 + \cdots + 2^{n-1}x^{n-1} + \cdots$ converges for what values of x ?

(A) $x = 0$ only

(B) $-\frac{1}{2} < x < \frac{1}{2}$ only

(C) $-1 < x < 1$ only

(D) $-2 < x < 2$ only

Answer

22. The Taylor series for $xe^{(2x^3)}$ centered at $x = 0$ is

(A) $\displaystyle\sum_{n=0}^{\infty} \frac{8^n x^{3n}}{n!}$

(B) $\displaystyle\sum_{n=0}^{\infty} \frac{8^n x^{3n+1}}{n!}$

(C) $\displaystyle\sum_{n=0}^{\infty} \frac{2^n x^{3n+1}}{n!}$

(D) $\displaystyle\sum_{n=0}^{\infty} \frac{2x^{3n+1}}{n!}$

Answer

23. If the length of a curve $y = f(x)$ from $x = a$ to $x = b$ is given by $L = \int_a^b \sqrt{e^{2x} + 2e^x + 2}\ dx$, then $f(x)$ could equal

(A) $2e^{2x} + 2e^x$

(B) $\frac{1}{2}e^{2x} + 2e^x + x$

(C) $e^x + 1$

(D) $e^x + x - 2$

Answer

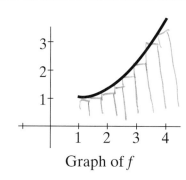

Graph of f

24. The graph of a function f is shown above for $1 \le x \le 4$. Of the following, which has the least value?

(A) $\int_1^4 f(x)\, dx$

(B) Left Riemann sum approximation of $\int_1^4 f(x)\, dx$ with 3 subdivisions of equal length

(C) Right Riemann sum approximation of $\int_1^4 f(x)\, dx$ with 3 subdivisions of equal length

(D) Midpoint Riemann sum approximation of $\int_1^4 f(x)\, dx$ with 3 subdivisions of equal length

Answer

25. If $\dfrac{dy}{dx} = e^x y$ and $y = 3$ when $x = 0$, then $y =$

(A) $\dfrac{3e^{e^x}}{e}$ (B) $3e^{e^x}$ (C) $\dfrac{1}{3}e^{e^x}$ (D) $\dfrac{3e^x}{e}$

$$e^x y = 3$$
$$0 = y = 3$$
$$= \dfrac{3e^{e^x}}{e}$$

Answer

26. $\displaystyle\int_{2}^{4} \dfrac{t+3}{(t-1)(t-2)}\, dt$ is found by using which of the following limits?

(A) $\displaystyle\lim_{b \to 2^-}\int_{b}^{4}\left(\dfrac{5}{t-2} - \dfrac{4}{t-1}\right) dt$

(B) $\displaystyle\lim_{b \to 2^+}\int_{b}^{4}\left(\dfrac{5}{t-2} - \dfrac{4}{t-1}\right) dt$

(C) $\displaystyle\lim_{b \to 2^-}\int_{b}^{4}\left(\dfrac{4}{t-1} - \dfrac{5}{t-2}\right) dt$

(D) $\displaystyle\lim_{b \to 2^+}\int_{b}^{4}\left(\dfrac{4}{t-1} - \dfrac{5}{t-2}\right) dt$

Answer

27. The average value of the function $f(x) = \cos\left(\frac{1}{2}x\right)$ on the closed interval $[-4, 0]$ is

(A) $-\frac{1}{2}\sin(2)$

(B) $-\frac{1}{4}\sin(2)$

(C) $\frac{1}{4}\sin(2)$

(D) $\frac{1}{2}\sin(2)$

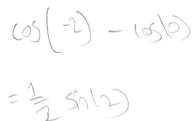

$\cos(-2) - \cos(0)$

$= \frac{1}{2}\sin(2)$

Answer

28. Using the substitution $u = \sqrt{2x}$, $\int_{2}^{8} \frac{dx}{\sqrt{2x}+1}$ is equivalent to

(A) $\int_{2}^{4} \frac{du}{u+1}$

(B) $\int_{2}^{8} \frac{du}{u+1}$

(C) $\int_{2}^{8} \frac{u\,du}{u+1}$

(D) $\int_{2}^{4} \frac{u\,du}{u+1}$

Answer

29. The volume of the solid formed by revolving the region bounded by the graphs of $y = 9$ and $y = (x - 3)^2$ about the line $y = 9$ is given by which of the following integrals?

(A) $\pi \int_0^6 (9^2 - (x - 3)^4)\, dx$

(B) $2\pi \int_0^3 (9 - (x - 3)^2)^2\, dx$

(C) $\pi \int_0^6 ((x - 3)^4 - 9^2)\, dx$

(D) $2\pi \int_0^3 (9 - (x - 3)^2)\, dx$

$$2\pi \int_1^4 \left(3 - (4-3)^2\right)^2 dy$$

$$2\pi \int_0^3 \left(4 - (x^2 + 6x - 9)\right)^2 dx$$

$$= 2\pi \int_0^3 \left(9 - (x-3)^2\right)^2 dx$$

Answer

30. Which of the following gives the total area of the region enclosed by the graph of the polar curve $r = 1 + \cos \theta$?

(A) $\int_0^\pi (1 + \cos^2 \theta)\, d\theta$

(B) $\int_0^\pi (1 + \cos \theta)^2\, d\theta$

(C) $\int_0^{2\pi} (1 + \cos \theta)^2\, d\theta$

(D) $\frac{1}{2} \int_0^{2\pi} (1 + \cos^2 \theta)\, d\theta$

$$\int_0^{2\pi - \pi}$$

$$= \int_0^\pi (1 + \cos \theta)^2\, \frac{d\theta}{2}$$

Answer

SECTION I PART B

A GRAPHING CALCULATOR IS REQUIRED FOR SOME QUESTIONS IN THIS SECTION.

Directions: Solve each of the following problems, using available space for scratch work. After examining the form of the choices, decide which is the best of the choices given. Do not spend too much time on any one problem.

In this exam:

(1) The exact numerical value of the correct answer does not always appear among the choices given. When this happens, select from among the choices the number that best approximates the exact numerical value.

(2) Unless otherwise specified, the domain of a function f is assumed to be the set of all real numbers x for which $f(x)$ is a real number.

(3) The inverse of a trigonometric function f may be indicated using the inverse function notation f^{-1} or with the prefix "arc" (e.g., $\sin^{-1}x = \arcsin x$)

31. Let f be the function given by $f(x) = \tan x$ and let g be the function given by $g(x) = x^2$. At what value of x in the interval $0 \le x \le \pi$ do the graphs of f and g have parallel tangent lines?

(A) 0.660   (B) 2.083   (C) 2.194   (D) 2.207

Answer

32. Given function f such that $\lim\limits_{h \to 0} \dfrac{f(x+h) - f(x-h)}{h} = 8 - 6x$.

Which of the following statements would be true?

    I. $f'(0) = 8$

    II. $f''(0) < 0$

    III. $f'''(0) = 0$

(A) I and II only

(B) I and III only

(C) II and III only

(D) I, II, and III

Answer

33. Let f be the function given by $f(x) = 3 + \int_0^x \cos(t^2)\, dt$. What is the least positive number a, for which $f'(a) = 0$?

(A) 1   (B) 1.253   (C) 1.571   (D) 1.772

Answer

34. The base of a solid is the region enclosed by the ellipse $4x^2 + y^2 = 1$. If all plane cross sections perpendicular to the x-axis are semicircles, then its volume is

(A) $\frac{\pi}{6}$ (B) $\frac{\pi}{4}$ (C) $\frac{\pi}{3}$ (D) $\frac{2\pi}{3}$

Answer

35. If f is differentiable and increasing on the interval $[0,b]$ and c is the number guaranteed by the Mean Value Theorem on this interval, then which statement must be true?

(A) $f'(c) = \dfrac{f(b)}{b}$

(B) $f'(c) = 0$

(C) $f'(c) > 0$

(D) $f'(x)$ changes sign at $x = c$.

Answer

36. Let $R(x)$ be the radius of a round pipe that drains water from a dam, where x is measured in feet from the dam. Which choice best explains the meaning of $\pi \displaystyle\int_{10,000}^{30,000} (R(x))^2 dx$?

(A) The amount of water in square feet that the pipe can hold in the section from 10,000 to 30,000 feet from the dam.

(B) The amount of water in cubic feet that the pipe can hold in the section from 10,000 to 30,000 feet from the dam.

(C) The amount of water in cubic feet flowing through the pipe from 10,000 to 30,000 feet.

(D) The amount of water in cubic feet in any 20,000-foot section of the pipe.

Answer

x	$f(x)$	$f'(x)$
1	8	-2
2	5	-4
3	1	-5

37. The table above gives selected values of a function, $f(x)$, with $f'(x) < 0$ and $f''(x) < 0$. If $g(x) = f^{-1}(x)$, what is the value of $g'(1)$?

(A) $-\dfrac{1}{5}$ (B) $-\dfrac{1}{2}$ (C) $\dfrac{1}{5}$ (D) $\dfrac{1}{2}$

Answer

38. The first and second derivatives of function f are positive for all values of x in the interval $[0,4]$. If $f(1) = 2$, $f'(1) = 2$, and $f''(1) = 2$, which of the following could be the value of $f(2)$?

(A) 2   (B) 3   (C) 4   (D) 5

Answer

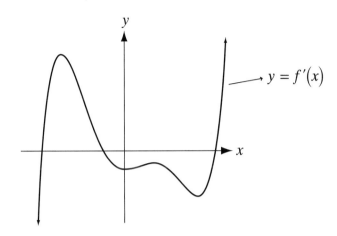

39. The figure above shows the graph of the <u>derivative</u> of a polynomial function f. How many points of inflection does the graph of f have?

(A) One   (B) Two   (C) Three   (D) Four

Answer

x	$f'(x)$
0.998	0.980
0.999	0.995
1.000	1.000
1.001	0.995
1.002	0.980

40. The table above gives values of the derivative of a function f. Based on this information, it appears that in the interval covered by the table

(A) f has a point of inflection.
(B) f is increasing and concave down everywhere.
(C) f is increasing and concave up everywhere.
(D) f is decreasing and concave up everywhere.

Answer

41. The graph of the third-degree Maclaurin polynomial for $\sin(x)$ intersects the graph of $y = x^2 - 1$ at approximately

(A) 0.879   (B) 1.066   (C)   1.262   (D) 1.394

Answer

42. The amount, $A(t)$, of a certain item produced in a factory is given by

$$A(t) = 63 + 90(t - 1) - (t - 3)^3$$

where t is the number of hours of production beginning at 8:00 am and ending at 4:00 pm. At what time is the rate of production at its maximum?

(A) 10:00 am   (B) 11:00 am   (C) 1:00 pm   (D) 3:00 pm

Answer

43. If $f(x) = e^x \ln x$, then $f'(e) =$

(A) $e^{e+1} + e^e$ (B) $e^{e-1} + e^e$ (C) $e^e + e$ (D) $e^e + \dfrac{1}{e}$

Answer

44. A population increases according to the equation $P(t) = 6000 - 5500e^{-0.159t}$ for $t \geq 0$,
t measured in years. This population will approach a limiting value as time goes on. During which year will the population reach <u>half</u> of this limiting value?

(A) Second

(B) Third

(C) Fourth

(D) Eighth

Answer

x	$f(x)$	$f'(x)$	$f''(x)$
1	−1	−2	−1
3	−5	−3	−2

45. For the twice differentiable function f the table above gives selected values of $f(x)$, $f'(x)$ and $f''(x)$. If $\displaystyle\int_1^3 f(x)\, dx = -4$, what is the value of $\displaystyle\int_1^3 x^2 f''(x)\, dx$?

(A) −5   (B) −3   (C) 3   (D) 5

Answer

FREE-RESPONSE QUESTIONS — GENERAL INSTRUCTIONS

For cach part of Section II, you may wish to look over the problems before starting to work on them. It is not expected that everyone will be able to complete all parts of all problems. All problems are given equal weight, but the parts of a particular problem are not necessarily given equal weight.

YOU SHOULD WRITE ALL WORK FOR EACH PART OF EACH PROBLEM IN THE SPACE PROVIDED FOR THAT PART. Be sure to write clearly and legibly. If you make an error, you may save time by crossing it out rather than trying to erase it. Erased or crossed-out work will not be graded. Manage your time carefully.

- Show all your work, even though a question may not explicitly remind you to do so. Clearly label any functions, graphs, tables, or other objects that you use. Your work will be graded on the correctness and completeness of your methods as well as your answers. Answers without supporting work will usually not receive credit.

- Justifications require that you give mathematical (noncalculator) reasons.

- Your work must be expressed in standard mathematical notation rather than calculator syntax. For example, $\int_1^5 x^2\,dx$ may not be written as fnInt(X^2, X, 1, 5).

- Unless otherwise specified, answers (numeric or algebraic) need not be simplified.

- If you use decimal approximations in calculations, your work will be graded on accuracy. Unless otherwise specified, your final answers should be accurate to three places after the decimal point.

- Unless otherwise specified, the domain of a function f is assumed to be the set of all real numbers x for which $f(x)$ is a real number.

SECTION II PART A: 30 Minutes, Questions 1,2

A graphing calculator is required.

During the timed portion for Part A, you may work only on the problems in Part A. Write your solution to each part of each problem in the space provided.

On Part A, you are permitted to use your calculator to solve an equation, find the derivative of a function at a point, or calculate the value of a definite integral. However, you must clearly indicate the setup of your programs, you must show the mathematical steps necessary to produce your results.

Do not go on to Part B until you are told to do so.

SECTION II PART B: 60 Minutes, Questions 3,4,5,6

Write your solution to each part of each problem in the space provided for that part. During the timed portion for Part B, you may continue to work on the problems in Part A without the use of any calculator.

Section II Part A: Graphing calculator is required for these problems.

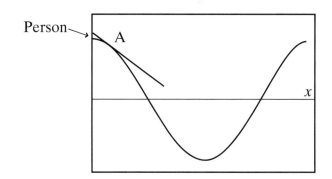

1. As shown in the figure above a person whose eye level is 5 feet above the ground stands

on the top of a hill overlooking a valley. The shape of the valley is modeled by the graph

of $f(x) = 50 \cos\left(\dfrac{x}{100}\right)$. The person's line of sight is tangent to the side of the hill at point A

$\left(a, 50 \cos\left(\dfrac{a}{100}\right)\right)$.

(a) Write an equation of the tangent line in terms of the coordinates of point A.
(b) Find the value of a.
(c) Can the person see the top of a 25-foot tall flagpole located at the lowest point of the valley? Justify your answer.

(a) Write an equation of the tangent line in terms of the coordinates of point A.

(b)   Find the value of *a*.

(c)   Can the person see the top of a 25-foot tall flagpole located at the lowest point of the valley? Justify your answer.

2. Two particles move in the xy-plane. For time $0 \leq t \leq 2\pi$, the position of particle A is given by $x(t) = \cos t$ and $y(t) = t$, and the position of particle B is given by $x(t) = \sin t$ and $y(t) = t$.

   (a)   In the viewing window provided below, sketch the path of particles A and B. Label the paths A and B and indicate with arrows the direction of each particle along its path.

   (b)   Find the velocity vector for each particle.

   (c)   At $t = 5$, which particle is moving faster to the right? Justify your answer.

   (d)   At $t = 5$, which particle's upward speed is greater? Justify your answer.

   (a)   In the viewing window provided below, sketch the path of particles A and B. Label the paths A and B and indicate with arrows the direction of each particle along its path.

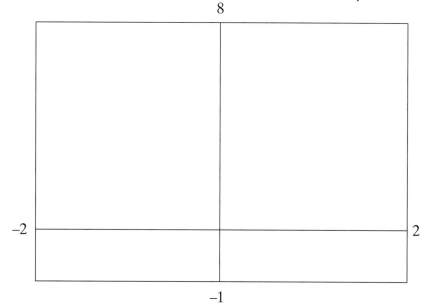

(b)   Find the velocity vector for each particle.

(c)   At $t = 5$, which particle is moving faster to the right? Justify your answer.

(d)   At $t = 5$, which particle's upward speed is greater? Justify your answer.

Section II Part B: No calculator is allowed for these problems.

3. For $0 \le t \le 4$, a particle is moving along the x-axis. The particle's position is given by
$$x(t) = 7t - 4t^2 + \int_0^t s^2 \, ds.$$

   (a) Find the position and velocity of the particle when $t = 3$.
   (b) At $t = 3$ what is the speed of the particle? Is the speed increasing or decreasing? Give a reason for your answer.
   (c) In the interval $(0,4)$ the particle changes direction once. Find the value of t when this change of direction occurs.
   (d) What is the value of t for which the particle is farthest right and at which it is farthest left? Justify your answer.

   (a) Find the position and velocity of the particle when $t = 3$.

   (b) At $t = 3$ what is the speed of the particle? Is the speed increasing or decreasing? Give a reason for your answer.

(c)   In the interval $(0,4)$ the particle changes direction once. Find the value of t when this change of direction occurs.

(d)   What is the value of t for which the particle is farthest right and at which it is farthest left? Justify your answer.

4. Let R be the region to the right of $x = 1$ between the x-axis and the graph of $y = \dfrac{1}{x^2}$ and let S be the region to the right of $x = 1$ between horizontal line $y = 1$ and the graph of $y = \dfrac{1}{x^2}$.

   (a)   Write an improper integral that gives the area of region R and find the value (if any) to which it converges.

   (b)   Write an improper integral that gives the area of region S and find the value (if any) to which it converges.

   (c)   The region R is the base of a solid. For this solid every cross section perpendicular to the x-axis is a square. Write an improper integral that gives the volume of this solid and find the value (if any) to which it converges.

   (a)   Write an improper integral that gives the area of region R and find the value (if any) to which it converges.

(b)   Write an improper integral that gives the area of region S and find the value (if any) to which it converges.

(c)   The region R is the base of a solid. For this solid every cross section perpendicular to the x-axis is a square. Write an improper integral that gives the volume of this solid and find the value (if any) to which it converges.

5. Consider the differential equation $\dfrac{dy}{dx} = xy^2$.

(a) On the axes provided, sketch a slope field for the given differential equation at the nine points indicated.

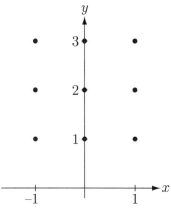

(b) If $y(1) = 1$, find $\lim\limits_{x \to 1} \dfrac{y-1}{x^2-1}$. Show the work that leads to your answer.

(c) Find the particular solution of the differential equation that satisfies the initial condition $y(1) = 1$.

(d) State the equations for which the particular solution of the differential equation in part (c) have one or more
    (i) horizontal asymptotes and/or
    (ii) vertical asymptotes
Justify your answer.

___

(a) On the axes provided, sketch a slope field for the given differential equation at the nine points indicated.

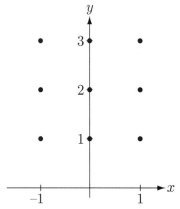

(b)   If $y(1) = 1$, find $\lim\limits_{x \to 1} \dfrac{y-1}{x^2-1}$. Show the work that leads to your answer.

(c)   Find the particular solution of the differential equation that satisfies the initial condition $y(1) = 1$.

(d)   State the equations for which the particular solution of the differential equation in part (c) have one or more
    (i) horizontal asymptotes and/or
    (ii) vertical asymptotes
Justify your answer.

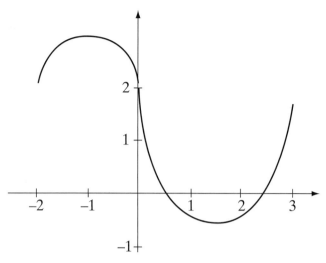

The graph of $f(x)$

6. Let f be a continuous function defined on the closed interval $[-2,3]$. The graph of f consists of a semicircle and a semi-ellipse, as shown above. Let $G(x) = G(-2) + \int_{-2}^{x} f(t)\, dt.$

   (a) On what intervals, if any, is G concave down? Justify your answer.
   (b) If the equation of the line tangent to the graph of $G(x)$ at the point where $x = 0$ is $y = mx + 7$, what is the value of m and the value of $G(0)$? Justify your answer.
   (c) If the average value of f on the interval $0 \le x \le 3$ is zero, find the value of $G(3)$. Show your work that leads to your answer.

   _____

   (a) On what intervals, if any, is G concave down? Justify your answer.

(b)   If the equation of the line tangent to the graph of $G(x)$ at the point where $x = 0$ is $y = mx + 7$, what is the value of m and the value of $G(0)$? Justify your answer.

(c)   If the average value of f on the interval $0 \leq x \leq 3$ is zero, find the value of $G(3)$. Show your work that leads to your answer.

SAMPLE EXAMINATION II
SECTION I PART A

NO CALCULATOR IS ALLOWED IN THIS SECTION.

Directions: Solve each of the following problems, using the available space for scratch work. After examining the form of the choices, decide which is the best of the choices given. Do not spend too much time on any one problem.

In this exam:

(1) Unless otherwise specified, the domain of a function f is assumed to be the set of all real numbers x for which $f(x)$ is a real number.

(2) The inverse of a trigonometric function f may be indicated using the inverse function notation f^{-1} or with the prefix "arc" (e.g., $\sin^{-1}x = \arcsin x$)

1. For differentiable functions f and g, $f(2x) = g(4x)$ for $x \geq 0$. Which of the following statements is necessarily true?

   (A) $f'(2) = g'(4)$

   (B) $f'(2) = 2g'(4)$

   (C) $2f'(2) = g'(4)$

   (D) $f'(2) = 4g'(4)$

Answer

x	-2	-1	0	1	2
$f(x)$	a	b	c	d	e
$f'(x)$	2	4	6	8	10

2. The table above gives values of a function f and its derivative at selected values of x. If f' is continuous on $[-2,2]$, what is the average value of f' on the closed interval $[-2,2]$?

   (A) $\dfrac{e-a}{4}$ (B) $\dfrac{a-e}{4}$ (C) $\dfrac{a-e}{8}$ (D) $\dfrac{e-a}{8}$

Answer

3. Let C be the curve defined by the parametric equations $x(t) = 2t^2 + t - 1$ and $y(t) = t^2 - 3t + 1$ for $-\infty < t < \infty$. For what value of t will the line tangent to the graph of C have a slope of 4 ?

(A) $-\dfrac{1}{2}$ (B) $-\dfrac{2}{7}$ (C) 2   (D) $\dfrac{13}{4}$

Answer

4. If $f(x) = (2 + 3x)^4$, then the fourth derivative of f at $x = 1$ is

(A) $4!(3)$ (B) $4!(3^4)$ (C) $4!(3^5)$ (D) $4!(5)$

Answer

5. At what values of x does $f(x) = x^4 - 8x^2$ have a relative minimum?

(A) 0 and -2 only

(B) 0 and 2 only

(C) -2 and 2 only

(D) $-2, 0$, and 2

Answer

6. $\displaystyle \int_1^e x^2 \ln(x)\, dx =$

(A) $\dfrac{4e^3 + 1}{9}$

(B) $\dfrac{4e^3 + 1}{3}$

(C) $\dfrac{2e^3 + 1}{9}$

(D) $\dfrac{2e^3 + 1}{3}$

Answer

7. What is the radius of convergence of the series $\displaystyle\sum_{n=0}^{\infty} \frac{(x-1)^{2n}}{6^n}$?

(A) $\dfrac{\sqrt{6}}{2}$ (B) $\sqrt{6}$ (C) $2\sqrt{6}$ (D) 6

Answer

8. The function $y = x^4 + bx^2 + 8x + 1$ has a horizontal tangent and a point of inflection for the same value of x. What must be the value of b ?

(A) −6   (B) −1   (C) 1   (D) 6

Answer

9. Let $y = f(x)$ be the solution to the differential equation $\dfrac{dy}{dx} = y - x$. The point $(5,1)$ is on the graph of the solution to this differential equation. What is the approximation of $f(6)$ if Euler's Method is used, starting at $x = 5$ with a step size of 0.5 ?

(A) −4.25   (B) −3.25   (C) −2.75   (D) −1.25

Answer

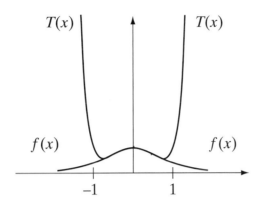

10. The figure above shows the graph of $y = f(x)$ and $y = T(x)$ where $T(x)$ is a Taylor polynomial for $f(x)$ centered at zero. Which of the following statements must be true?

    I. $T(0.5)$ is a good approximation for $f(0.5)$.

    II. $T(1.5)$ is a good approximation for $f(1.5)$.

    III. $T(0) = f(0)$

(A) I only

(B) III only

(C) I and II only

(D) I and III only

Answer

11. $\displaystyle \lim_{x \to 2} \frac{x^2 - 4}{\displaystyle\int_2^x \cos(\pi t)\, dt}$ is

(A) 0   (B) 2   (C) 4   (D) nonexistent

Answer

12. Which of the following improper integrals converge?

I. $\displaystyle\int_0^\infty e^{-x}\, dx$

II. $\displaystyle\int_0^1 \frac{1}{x^2}\, dx$

III. $\displaystyle\int_0^1 \frac{1}{\sqrt{x}}\, dx$

(A) I only

(B) III only

(C) II and III only

(D) I and III only

Answer

13. If $x + y = xy$, then $\dfrac{dy}{dx}$ is

(A) $\dfrac{1}{x-1}$ (B) $\dfrac{1-y}{x-1}$ (C) $\dfrac{y-1}{x-1}$ (D) $\dfrac{2-xy}{y}$

Answer

14. If f and g are differentiable functions defined for all real numbers, which of the following definite integrals is equal to $f(g(4)) - f(g(2))$?

(A) $\displaystyle\int_2^4 f'(g(x))\, dx$

(B) $\displaystyle\int_2^4 f(g(x))\, g'(x)\, dx$

(C) $\displaystyle\int_2^4 f'(g(x))\, g'(x)\, dx$

(D) $\displaystyle\int_2^4 f(g'(x))\, g'(x)\, dx$

Answer

15. The velocity of a particle moving along the y-axis is given by $v(t) = 8 - 2t$ for $t \geq 0$.
The particle moves upward until it reaches the origin and then moves downward. The position of the particle at any time t is given by

(A) $-t^2 + 8t - 16$

(B) $-t^2 + 8t + 16$

(C) $2t^2 - 8t - 16$

(D) $8t - t^2$

Answer

16. If the substitution $u = \sqrt{x-1}$ is made, the integral $\displaystyle\int_2^5 \frac{\sqrt{x-1}}{x}\,dx =$

(A) $\displaystyle\int_2^5 \frac{2u^2}{u^2+1}\,du$

(B) $\displaystyle\int_1^2 \frac{u^2}{u^2+1}\,du$

(C) $\displaystyle\int_2^5 \frac{u}{u^2+1}\,du$

(D) $\displaystyle\int_1^2 \frac{2u^2}{u^2+1}\,du$

Answer

17. The first three nonzero terms in the Maclaurin series of xe^{-x} are

(A) $x - x^2 - \dfrac{x^3}{2!}$

(B) $x - x^2 + \dfrac{x^3}{2!}$

(C) $x + x^2 + \dfrac{x^3}{2!}$

(D) $1 - x + \dfrac{x^2}{2!}$

Answer

18. If $\displaystyle\int_0^2 \left(2x^3 - kx^2 + 2k\right)\,dx = 12$, then k must equal

(A) -3 (B) 1   (C) 2   (D) 3

Answer

19. $\displaystyle\sum_{n=1}^{\infty}\left(\frac{1}{2}\right)^{2n}$ is

(A) $\dfrac{1}{3}$ (B) $\dfrac{1}{2}$ (C) 1   (D) 2

Answer

20. For $|x| < 1$, the derivative of $y = \ln\sqrt{1-x^2}$ is

(A) $\dfrac{x}{1-x^2}$ (B) $\dfrac{x}{x^2-1}$ (C) $\dfrac{-1}{x^2-1}$ (D) $\dfrac{1}{\sqrt{1-x^2}}$

Answer

21. The Taylor series for $(x-1)\ln(x)$ centered at $x = 1$ is

(A) $\displaystyle\sum_{n=0}^{\infty} \frac{(-1)^{n+2}(x-1)^{n+2}}{n+2}$

(B) $\displaystyle\sum_{n=0}^{\infty} \frac{(-1)^{n}(x-1)^{n+2}}{(n+1)!}$

(C) $\displaystyle\sum_{n=2}^{\infty} \frac{(-1)^{n}n(x-1)^{n}}{n!}$

(D) $\displaystyle\sum_{n=2}^{\infty} \frac{(-1)^{n}(x-1)^{n}}{n-1}$

Answer

22. What are the values of x for which the graph of $y = x^3 - 6x^2$ is concave downward?

(A) $x > 2$ (B) $x < 2$ (C) $x < 0$ (D) $x > 4$

Answer

x	2	8
$f(x)$	1	3
$f'(x)$	2	12
$g(x)$	2	−6
$g'(x)$	4	−12

23. The table above gives the values of f, f', g, and g' for selected values of x.

    What is the value of $\displaystyle\int_2^8 \frac{f(x)\,g'(x) - g(x)\,f'(x)}{(f(x))^2}\,dx$?

    (A) $-\dfrac{1}{4}$ (B) $-\dfrac{1}{3}$ (C) -3 (D) -4

Answer

24. Which of the following series are convergent?

    I. $1 + \dfrac{1}{2\sqrt{2}} + \dfrac{1}{3\sqrt{3}} + \cdots + \dfrac{1}{n\sqrt{n}} + \cdots$

    II. $\dfrac{1}{1\cdot 2} + \dfrac{1}{2\cdot 3} + \dfrac{1}{3\cdot 4} + \cdots + \dfrac{1}{n(n+1)} + \cdots$

    III. $1 + \dfrac{1}{\ln 2} + \dfrac{1}{\ln 3} + \cdots + \dfrac{1}{\ln(n+1)} + \cdots$

    (A) I only

    (B) II only

    (C) I and II only

    (D) I, II, and III

Answer

25. For all x if $f(x) = \displaystyle\sum_{n-0}^{\infty} \frac{(-1)^{n+1} x^{2n+1}}{(2n+1)!}$, then $f'(x) =$

(A) $\displaystyle\sum_{n=0}^{\infty} \frac{(-1)^{n+1} x^{2n}}{(2n+1)!}$

(B) $\displaystyle\sum_{n=0}^{\infty} \frac{(-1)^{n+1} x^{2n}}{(2n)!}$

(C) $\displaystyle\sum_{n=0}^{\infty} \frac{(-1)^{n} x^{2n}}{(2n)!}$

(D) $\displaystyle\sum_{n=0}^{\infty} \frac{(-1)^{n} x^{2n}}{(2n+1)!}$

Answer

26. A <u>normal</u> line to the graph of a function f at the point $(x, f(x))$ is defined to be the line perpendicular to the tangent line at that point. An equation of the <u>normal</u> line to the curve $y = \sqrt[3]{x^2 - 1}$ at the point where $x = 3$ is

(A) $y + 12x = 38$

(B) $y + 2x = 4$

(C) $y + 2x = 8$

(D) $y - 2x = -4$

Answer

27. Which graph best represents the position of a particle, $s(t)$, as a function of time, if the particle's velocity and acceleration are both positive?

(A) $s(t)$

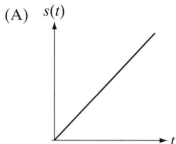

(B) $s(t)$

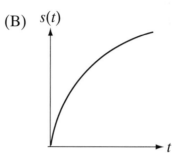

(C) $s(t)$

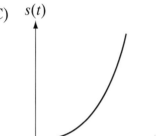

(D) $s(t)$

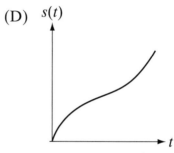

Answer

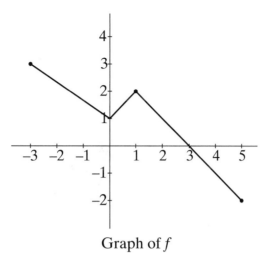

Graph of f

28. The graph of a piecewise linear function f is shown above. If $g(x) = \int_0^x f(t)\, dt$, which of the following has the greatest value?

(A) $g(-3)$ (B) $g(1)$ (C) $g(3)$ (D) $g(5)$

Answer

29. For the series $\displaystyle\sum_{n=1}^{\infty} \frac{\sin(n)}{n^2}$ which of the following statements is true?

(A) The series diverges.

(B) The series converges absolutely.

(C) The series converges conditionally.

(D) The series converges but not absolutely nor conditionally.

Answer

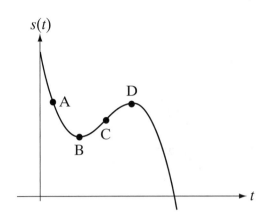

30. The graph above shows the distance $s(t)$ from a reference point of a particle moving on a number line, as a function of time. Which of the points marked is closest to the point where the acceleration first becomes negative?

(A) A   (B) B   (C) C   (D) D

Answer

SECTION I PART B

Directions: Solve each of the following problems, using available space for scratch work. After examining the form of the choices, decide which is the best of the choices given. Do not spend too much time on any one problem.

In this exam:

(1) The exact numerical value of the correct answer does not always appear among the choices given. When this happens, select from among the choices the number that best approximates the exact numerical value.

(2) Unless otherwise specified, the domain of a function f is assumed to be the set of all real numbers x for which $f(x)$ is a real number.

(3) The inverse of a trigonometric function f may be indicated using the inverse function notation f^{-1} or with the prefix "arc" (e.g., $\sin^{-1} x = \arcsin x$)

31. If the position of a particle moving in the *xy*-plane is given by the parametric equations $x(t) = 9 \cos t$ and $y(t) = 4 \sin t$ for $t \geq 0$, then at $t = 3$, the acceleration vector is

(A) $\langle -8.910, 0.564 \rangle$

(B) $\langle -8.910, -0.564 \rangle$

(C) $\langle 8.910, -0.564 \rangle$

(D) $\langle 8.910, 0.564 \rangle$

Answer

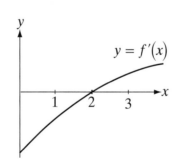

32. The graph of the derivative of a twice-differentiable function *f* is shown above. If $f(1) = -2$, which of the following is true?

(A) $f(2) < f'(2) < f''(2)$

(B) $f''(2) < f'(2) < f(2)$

(C) $f'(2) < f(2) < f''(2)$

(D) $f(2) < f''(2) < f'(2)$

Answer

33. Let f be a function that is everywhere differentiable. The value of $f'(x)$ is given for selected values of x in the table below.

x	−10	−5	0	5	10
$f'(x)$	−2	−1	0	1	2

If $f'(x)$ is always increasing, which statement about $f(x)$ must be true?

(A) $f(x)$ has a relative minimum at $x = 0$.

(B) $f(x)$ is concave downwards for all x.

(C) $f(x)$ has a point of inflection at $(0, f(0))$.

(D) $f(x)$ is an odd function.

Answer

34. An ice field is melting at the rate $M(t) = 4 - (\sin t)^3$ acre-feet per day, where t is measured in days. How many acre-feet of this ice field will melt from the beginning of day 1 $(t = 0)$ to the beginning of day 4 $(t = 3)$?

(A) 10.667   (B) 10.951   (C) 11.544   (D) 11.999

Answer

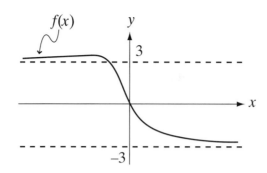

35. The figure above shows the graph of a function $f(x)$ which has horizontal asymptotes of $y = 3$ and $y = -3$. Which of the following statements are true?

   I. $f'(x) < 0$ for all $x \geq 0$

   II. $\lim_{x \to +\infty} f'(x) = 0$

   III. $\lim_{x \to -\infty} f'(x) = 3$

   (A) I only

   (B) II only

   (C) I and II only

   (D) I, II, and III

Answer

36. The <u>derivative</u> of f is given by $f'(x) = e^x\left(-x^3 + 3x\right) - 3$ for $0 \le x \le 5$.

At what value of x is $f(x)$ an absolute minimum?

(A) 0   (B) 0.618   (C) 1.623   (D) 5

Answer

x	$f(x)$
3.99800	1.15315
3.99900	1.15548
4.00000	1.15782
4.00100	1.16016
4.00200	1.16250

37. The table above gives values of a differentiable function f.
What is the approximate value of $f'(4)$?

(A) 0.00234

(B) 0.289

(C) 0.427

(D) 2.340

Answer

38. What is the length of the path described by the parametric equations $x(t) = \sin t$ and $y(t) = \cos(2t)$, where $0 \le t \le 2\pi$?

   (A) 15.708   (B) 9.294   (C) 6.097   (D) 5.916

Answer

39. In the interval $0 \le x \le 5$ the graphs of $y = \cos 2x$ and $y = \sin 3x$ intersect four times. Let $a, b, c,$ and d be the x-coordinates of these points so that $0 < a < b < c < d < 5$. Which of the definite integrals below has the greatest value?

   (A) $\displaystyle\int_0^a (\cos 2x - \sin 3x)\, dx$

   (B) $\displaystyle\int_a^b (\sin 3x - \cos 2x)\, dx$

   (C) $\displaystyle\int_b^c (\sin 3x - \cos 2x)\, dx$

   (D) $\displaystyle\int_c^d (\cos 2x - \sin 3x)\, dx$

Answer

40. The function $f(x) = \tan(3^x)$ has one zero in the closed interval $[0, 1.4]$. The derivative at this point is

(A) 0.411   (B) 1.042   (C) 3.451   (D) 3.763

Answer

x	0	1	2	3	4	5	6
$f(x)$	0	0.25	0.48	0.68	0.84	0.95	1

41. For the function whose values are given in the table above, $\int_0^6 f(x)\,dx$ is approximated by a Riemann sum using the value at the midpoint of each of three intervals of width 2.

The approximation is

(A) 2.64   (B) 3.64   (C) 3.76   (D) 4.64

Answer

42. $\dfrac{d}{dx}\displaystyle\int_{x}^{x^3} \sin\left(t^2\right) dt =$

    (A) $6x^2 \sin\left(x^3\right) - 2 \sin x$

    (B) $3x^2 \sin\left(x^6\right) - \sin\left(x^2\right)$

    (C) $6x^5 \sin\left(x^6\right) - 2x \sin\left(x^2\right)$

    (D) $2x^3 \cos\left(x^6\right) - 2x \cos\left(x^2\right)$

Answer

43. A tank is being filled with water at the rate of $300\sqrt{t}$ gallons per hour with $t > 0$ measured in hours. If the tank is originally empty, how many gallons of water are in the tank after 4 hours?

    (A)   600   (B)   900   (C)   1200   (D)   1600

Answer

44. The region in the first quadrant enclosed by the graphs of $y = x$ and $y = 2 \sin x$ is revolved about the x-axis. The volume of the solid generated is

(A) 1.433   (B) 5.811   (C) 6.678   (D) 13.355

Answer

45. The tangent line to the graph $y = e^{2-x}$ at the point $(1, e)$ intersects both coordinate axes. What is the area of the triangle formed by this tangent line and the coordinate axes?

(A) $2e$ (B) e^2 (C) $2e\sqrt{e}$ (D) $4e$

Answer

FREE-RESPONSE QUESTIONS — GENERAL INSTRUCTIONS

For each part of Section II, you may wish to look over the problems before starting to work on them. It is not expected that everyone will be able to complete all parts of all problems. All problems are given equal weight, but the parts of a particular problem are not necessarily given equal weight.

YOU SHOULD WRITE ALL WORK FOR EACH PART OF EACH PROBLEM IN THE SPACE PROVIDED FOR THAT PART. Be sure to write clearly and legibly. If you make an error, you may save time by crossing it out rather than trying to erase it. Erased or crossed-out work will not be graded. Manage your time carefully.

- Show all your work, even though a question may not explicitly remind you to do so. Clearly label any functions, graphs, tables, or other objects that you use. Your work will be graded on the correctness and completeness of your methods as well as your answers. Answers without supporting work will usually not receive credit.

- Justifications require that you give mathematical (noncalculator) reasons.

- Your work must be expressed in standard mathematical notation rather than calculator syntax. For example, $\int_1^5 x^2\,dx$ may not be written as fnInt(X^2, X, 1, 5).

- Unless otherwise specified, answers (numeric or algebraic) need not be simplified.

- If you use decimal approximations in calculations, your work will be graded on accuracy. Unless otherwise specified, your final answers should be accurate to three places after the decimal point.

- Unless otherwise specified, the domain of a function f is assumed to be the set of all real numbers x for which $f(x)$ is a real number.

SECTION II PART A: 30 Minutes, Questions 1,2

A graphing calculator is required.

During the timed portion for Part A, you may work only on the problems in Part A. Write your solution to each part of each problem in the space provided.

On Part A, you are permitted to use your calculator to solve an equation, find the derivative of a function at a point, or calculate the value of a definite integral. However, you must clearly indicate the setup of your programs, you must show the mathematical steps necessary to produce your results.

Do not go on to Part B until you are told to do so.

SECTION II PART B: 60 Minutes, Questions 3,4,5,6

Write your solution to each part of each problem in the space provided for that part. During the timed portion for Part B, you may continue to work on the problems in Part A without the use of any calculator.

Section II Part A: Graphing calculator is required for these problems.

---

1. A train travels along a straight track. Its velocity, $v(t)$, in miles per hour for the first half of the trip is given by $v(t) = -5t^2 + 20t + 25$, $0 \leq t \leq 5$, t is time in hours. During the second half of the trip its velocity is given by the values in the table below. Note that $v(9) = k$, $k < 0$.

t	5	6	7	8	9	10
$v(t)$	0	−25	−20	−50	k	−20

(a) How far did the train travel in the first half of the trip? Include units of measure.
(b) What was the acceleration at $t = 3$ hours? Include units of measure.
(c) If the train has returned to its starting point at $t = 10$ hours, using a right Riemann sum with $n = 5$ for $5 \leq t \leq 10$, estimate the value of k to the nearest whole number. Show how you arrived at your answer.

(a) How far did the train travel in the first half of the trip? Include units of measure.

(b)   What was the acceleration at $t = 3$ hours? Include units of measure.

(c)   If the train has returned to its starting point at $t = 10$ hours, using a right Riemann sum with $n = 5$ for $5 \le t \le 10$, estimate the value of k to the nearest whole number. Show how you arrived at your answer.

2. The temperature $T(x)$, in °F, in a small office building without air conditioning is given by
$T(x) = 73 - 14\cos\left(\dfrac{\pi(x - 3.4)}{12}\right)$, where x is the time elapsed since midnight, $0 \leq x \leq 24$.

To cool the building, the air conditioning is turned on when the temperature first reaches the

desired temperature T_0 and left on until the office closes at 6:00 p.m. (that is, when $x = 18$).

The cost per day, in dollars, of cooling is given by $C(x) = 0.16\displaystyle\int_x^{18}(T(x) - T_0)\,dx$ for $T(x) \geq T_0$.

(a) Estimated to the nearest half-hour, at what time will the temperature first reach 70°F ?
(b) Estimated to the nearest half-hour, at what time will the temperature first reach 77°F ?
(c) What is the cost per day of cooling the office if the desired temperature is 70°F ?
Show your reasoning.
(d) How much money is saved per day if the desired temperature is raised to 77°F ?

(a) Estimated to the nearest half-hour, at what time will the temperature first reach 70°F ?

(b) Estimated to the nearest half-hour, at what time will the temperature first reach 77°F ?

(c)   What is the cost per day of cooling the office if the desired temperature is 70°F? Show your reasoning.

(d)   How much money is saved per day if the desired temperature is raised to 77°F ?

t	0	2	5	9	13	15
$h'(t)$	0.4	0.5	0.7	1.0	1.1	1.3

3. A tank with a rectangular base measuring 10 inches by 20 inches is being filled with water at a variable rate. The depth of the water in the tank is given by a twice-differentiable function h of time, t, measured in minutes. The table above gives the rate of change, $h'(t)$, of the depth of the water in the tank for selected values of t over the time interval $0 \le t \le 15$. During this interval $h''(t) > 0$. When $t = 5$ minutes, the depth of the water is 6 inches.

(Note: The volume of the water in the tank is given by $V = lwh$.)

(a) Approximate the depth of the water in the tank at $t = 4$ minutes using the tangent line approximation at $t = 5$. Is your estimate greater than or less than the true value? Give a reason for your answer.

(b) Find the rate of change of the volume of the water in the tank at $t = 2$ minutes. Indicate units of measure.

(c) Use a left Riemann sum with five subintervals indicated by the table to approximate $\int_0^{15} h'(t)\, dt$. Using correct units, explain the meaning of $\int_0^{15} h'(t)\, dt$ in terms of the depth of the water in the tank.

(d) Is the approximation in part (c) greater than or less than $\int_0^{15} h'(t)\, dt$? Give a reason for your answer.

(a) Approximate the depth of the water in the tank at $t = 4$ minutes using the tangent line approximation at $t = 5$. Is your estimate greater than or less than the true value? Give a reason for your answer.

(b) Find the rate of change of the volume of the water in the tank at $t = 2$ minutes. Indicate units of measure.

(c) Use a left Riemann sum with five subintervals indicated by the table to approximate $\int_0^{15} h'(t)\, dt$. Using correct units, explain the meaning of $\int_0^{15} h'(t)\, dt$ in terms of the depth of the water in the tank.

(d) Is the approximation in part (c) greater than or less than $\int_0^{15} h'(t)\, dt$? Give a reason for your answer.

4. Consider the differential equation $\dfrac{dy}{dx} = \dfrac{y - y^2}{x}$ for all $x \neq 0$.

(a) Verify that $y = \dfrac{x}{x + C}$, $x \neq -C$ and $C \neq 0$ is a general solution for the given differential equation and show that all solutions contain $(0,0)$.

(b) Write an equation of the particular solution that contains the point $(1,2)$, and find the value of $\dfrac{dy}{dx}$ at $(0,0)$ for this solution.

(c) Write an equation of the vertical and horizontal asymptotes of the particular solution found in (b).

(d) The slope field for the given differential equation is provided. Sketch both branches of the particular solution curve that passes through the point $(1,2)$.

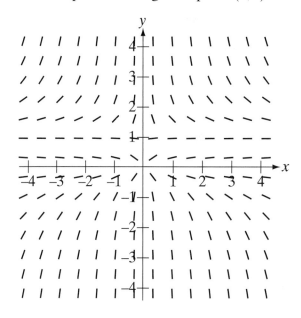

(a) Verify that $y = \dfrac{x}{x + C}$, $x \neq -C$ and $C \neq 0$ is a general solution for the given differential equation and show that all solutions contain $(0,0)$.

(b)   Write an equation of the particular solution that contains the point $(1,2)$, and find the value of $\dfrac{dy}{dx}$ at $(0,0)$ for this solution.

(c)   Write an equation of the vertical and horizontal asymptotes of the particular solution found in (b).

(d)   The slope field for the given differential equation is provided. Sketch both branches of the particular solution curve that passes through the point $(1,2)$.

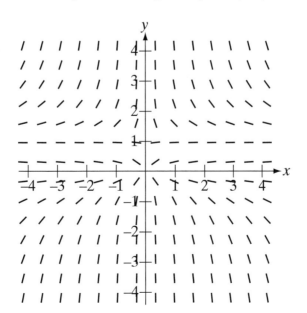

5. A particle moves along the curve defined by the parametric equations $x(t) = 2t$ and $y(t) = 36 - t^2$ for time t, $0 \leq t \leq 6$. A laser light on the particle points in the direction of motion and shines on the x-axis.

    (a)   What is the velocity vector of the particle?

    (b)   In terms of t, write an equation of the line tangent to the graph of the curve at the point $(2t, 36 - t^2)$.

    (c)   Express the x-coordinate of the point on the x-axis that the laser light hits as a function of t.

    (d)   At what speed is the laser light moving along the x-axis at time $t = 3$? Justify your answer.

    (a)   What is the velocity vector of the particle?

    (b)   In terms of t, write an equation of the line tangent to the graph of the curve at the point $(2t, 36 - t^2)$.

(c)   Express the *x*-coordinate of the point on the *x*-axis that the laser light hits as a function of *t*.

(d)   At what speed is the laser light moving along the *x*-axis at time $t = 3$? Justify your answer.

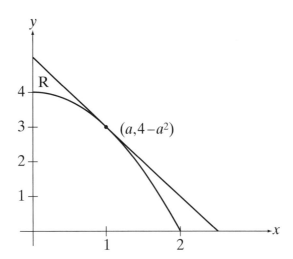

6. Let $f(x) = 4 - x^2$. Let R be the region in the first quadrant bounded by the graphs of f, its tangent line at $x = a$, and the y-axis.

(a) Write an equation of the tangent line in terms of a.
(b) Write an integral expression that gives the area of region R.
(c) Write an expression for the area of region R in terms of a, without an integral sign.
(d) Find the average value of the area of region R in terms of a.

(a) Write an equation of the tangent line in terms of a.

(b) Write an integral expression that gives the area of region R.

(c) Write an expression for the area of region R in terms of a, without an integral sign.

(d) Find the average value of the area of region R in terms of a.

SAMPLE EXAMINATION III
SECTION I PART A

NO CALCULATOR IS ALLOWED IN THIS SECTION.

Directions: Solve each of the following problems, using the available space for scratch work. After examining the form of the choices, decide which is the best of the choices given. Do not spend too much time on any one problem.

In this exam:

(1) Unless otherwise specified, the domain of a function f is assumed to be the set of all real numbers x for which $f(x)$ is a real number.

(2) The inverse of a trigonometric function f may be indicated using the inverse function notation f^{-1} or with the prefix "arc" (e.g., $\sin^{-1}x = \arcsin x$)

1. The area of the region between the graph of $y = 3x^2 + 2x$ and the x-axis from $x = 1$ to $x = 3$ is

(A) 36   (B) 34   (C) 31   (D) 28

Answer

2. $\lim\limits_{x \to 0} \dfrac{x}{e^{2x} - 1}$ is

(A) 0   (B) $\dfrac{1}{2}$ (C) 1   (D) nonexistent

$$\frac{1}{2 \cdot e^x} = \frac{1}{2}$$

Answer

3. Over a period of time in a national preserve the population of deer, P, changes at a rate based on the logistic differential equation $\dfrac{dP}{dt} = 0.25P(1200 - P)$, where t is given in years. For what values of P will the population of deer increase at a decreasing rate?

(A) $0 < P < 300$

(B) $300 < P < 600$

(C) $600 < P < 1200$

(D) $P > 1200$

Answer

4. A particle moves in the xy-plane so that at any time t, $t > 0$, its coordinates are $x = e^t \sin t$ and $y = e^t \cos t$. At $t = \pi$, its velocity vector is

(A) $\langle e^{\pi}, -e^{\pi} \rangle$

(B) $\langle -e^{\pi}, e^{\pi} \rangle$

(C) $\langle e^{\pi}, e^{\pi} \rangle$

(D) $\langle -e^{\pi}, -e^{\pi} \rangle$

Answer

5. A particle moves along a straight line so that its velocity is given by $v(t) = t^2$. How far does the particle travel between $t = 1$ and $t = 3$?

(A) $\dfrac{26}{3}$ (B) 8   (C) 26   (D) 27

Answer

x	0	1	2	3	4	5
$f(x)$	-8	-5	-2	0	2	1
$f'(x)$	2	4	3	2	0	-3

6. The table above gives values of a function f and its derivative at selected values of x. If f' is continuous on $[0,5]$, what is the value of $\displaystyle\int_1^4 f'(x)\, dx$?

(A) -4 (B) 2   (C) 7   (D) 9

Answer

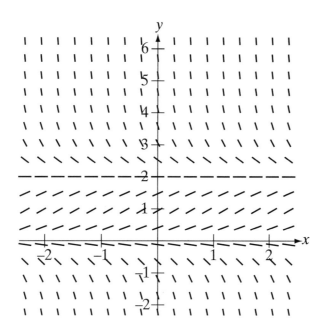

7. The slope field for a differential equation $\dfrac{dy}{dx} = f(y)$ is shown in the figure above.

Which statement is true about $y(x)$?

   I. If $y(0) > 2$, then $\lim\limits_{x \to \infty} y(x) \approx 2$.

   II. If $0 < y(0) < 2$, then $\lim\limits_{x \to \infty} y(x) \approx 2$.

   III. If $y(0) < 0$, then $\lim\limits_{x \to \infty} y(x) \approx 2$.

(A) I only

(B) III only

(C) I and II only

(D) I, II, and III

Answer

8. $\int_1^3 \dfrac{x}{x^2+1}\, dx =$

(A) $\dfrac{1}{2}\ln 5$ (B) $\ln 5$ (C) $2\ln 5$ (D) $\ln\left(\dfrac{5}{2}\right)$

Answer

9. Which one of the following is the value of the slope of the line tangent to the polar curve $r = \cos(2\theta)$ at $\theta = \dfrac{\pi}{6}$?

(A) $-\sqrt{3}$ (B) $-\dfrac{\sqrt{3}}{2}$ (C) 0 (D) $\dfrac{\sqrt{3}}{7}$

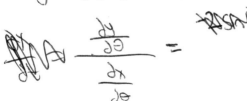

Answer

10. $\int_{1}^{\infty} x^{-\frac{5}{4}} dx$ is

(A) 4   (B) $\frac{5}{4}$ (C) $\frac{1}{4}$ (D) divergent

$$\lim_{b \to \infty} \int_{1}^{b} x^{-5/4}$$

$$-4x^{-1/4} \Big|_{1}^{b}$$

Answer

11. A function f is continuous on the closed interval $[4,6]$ and twice differentiable on the open interval $(4,6)$. If $f'(5) = -3$, and f is concave downwards on the given interval, which of the following could be a table of values for f?

(A)

x	$f(x)$
4	8
5	4
6	0

(B)

x	$f(x)$
4	8
5	6
6	2

(C)

x	$f(x)$
4	8
5	6
6	5

(D)

x	$f(x)$
4	8
5	3
6	2

Answer

12. Which of the following are the coordinates of the point where the slope of the line tangent to the graph of $f(x) = \dfrac{kx-3}{x+2}$ equals 1 when $x = k$?

(A) $(-3, -6)$ (B) $(-1, -2)$ (C) $\left(2, \dfrac{1}{4}\right)$ (D) $\left(3, \dfrac{6}{5}\right)$

Answer

x	5	6	9	11	12
$f(x)$	10	7	11	12	8

13. A function f is continuous on the closed interval $[5, 12]$ and differentiable on the open interval $(5, 12)$ and f has the values given in the table above. Using the subintervals $[5, 6], [6, 9], [9, 11]$, and $[11, 12]$, what is the right Riemann sum approximation to $\displaystyle\int_{5}^{12} f(x)\, dx$?

(A) 64   (B) 65   (C) 66   (D) 72

Answer

14. $\displaystyle\sum_{k=0}^{\infty}\left(-\frac{\pi}{3}\right)^{k}$ is

(A) $\dfrac{1}{1-\frac{\pi}{3}}$ (B) $\dfrac{1}{1+\frac{\pi}{3}}$ (C) $\dfrac{\frac{\pi}{3}}{1+\frac{\pi}{3}}$ (D) divergent

Answer

15. The following statements concerning the location of an extreme value of a twice-differentiable funtion, f, are all true. Which statement also includes the correct justification?

(A) The function has a maximum at $x = 5$ because $f'(x) < 0$ for $x < 5$ and $f'(x) > 0$ for $x > 5$.

(B) The function has a minimum at $x = 3$ because the tangent line at $x = 3$ is horizontal.

(C) The function has a minimum at $x = 3$ because $f'(x) < 0$ for $x < 3$ and $f'(x) > 0$ for $x > 3$.

(D) The function has a minimum at $x = 3$ because $f''(3) < 0$.

Answer

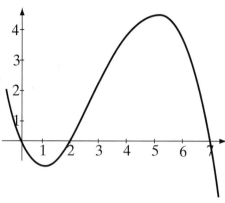

Graph of f

16. The graph of a differentiable function f is shown above. The graph has a relative minimum at $x = 1$ and a relative maximum at $x = 5$. Let g be the function defined by $g(x) = \int_0^x f(t)\, dt$. For what value of x does the graph of g change from concave up to concave down?

(A) 1 (B) 2 (C) 5 (D) 7

Answer

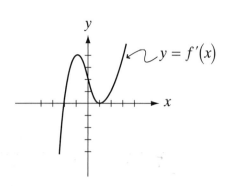

17. The graph of the <u>derivative</u> of f is shown in the figure above. Which of the following could be the graph of f?

(A)

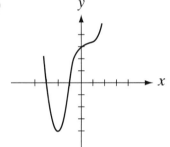

(B)

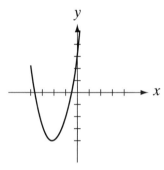

(C)

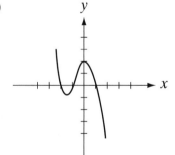

(D)

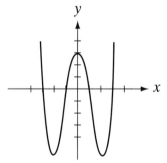

Answer

18. If $x = t - t^2$ and $y = \sqrt{2t + 5}$, then $\dfrac{dy}{dx}$ at $t = 2$ is

(A) -9 (B) -1 (C) $-\dfrac{1}{9}$ (D) $-\dfrac{1}{18}$

$y = (2t+5)^{1/2}$

$y = \frac{1}{2}(2t+5) \cdot 2 = (2t+5)^{-1/2} = (9)^{-1/2} = \frac{1}{3}$

$\dfrac{dx}{1-2t} \qquad = -3 \qquad \dfrac{\frac{1}{3}}{\frac{-3}{1}} = -\dfrac{1}{9}$

Answer

---

19. If $f'(x) = \dfrac{(x+2)^2 (x^2 - 1)}{3}$ and $g(x) = f(\sqrt{x+1})$, what is the value of $g'(3)$?

(A) 32   (B) 16   (C) 4   (D) $\dfrac{1}{4}$

Answer

20. At each point (x,y) on a certain curve, the slope of the curve is $4xy$. If the curve contains the point $(0,4)$, then its equation is

(A) $y = 4e^{2x^2}$

(B) $y = e^{2x^2} + 3$

(C) $y = e^{2x^2} + 4$

(D) $y = 2x^2 + 4$

Answer

21. $\int \frac{dx}{x^2 - 9} =$

(A) $\frac{1}{3} \ln \left| \frac{x+3}{x-3} \right| + C$

(B) $\ln \left| x^2 - 9 \right| + C$

(C) $\frac{1}{6} \ln \left| \frac{x+3}{x-3} \right| + C$

(D) $\frac{1}{6} \ln \left| \frac{x-3}{x+3} \right| + C$

$1 = A(x+3) + B(x-3)$

$\qquad = \int \frac{A}{(x-3)} + \frac{B}{(x+3)}$

$X = -3$

$1 = -6B$

$\qquad B = -\frac{1}{6}$

$X = 3$

$1 = 6A$

$\qquad A = \frac{1}{6}$

$\int \frac{\frac{1}{6}}{x-3} + \frac{-\frac{1}{6}}{x+3}$

Answer

22. Which of the following definite integrals gives the length of the graph of $y = e^{(e^x)}$ between $x = 0$ and $x = 1$?

(A) $\displaystyle\int_0^1 \sqrt{1 + e^{2(x+e^x)}}\, dx$

(B) $\displaystyle\int_0^1 \sqrt{1 + e^{(x+e^x)}}\, dx$

(C) $\displaystyle\int_0^1 \sqrt{1 + e^{4x}}\, dx$

(D) $\displaystyle\int_0^1 \sqrt{1 + e^{2e^x}}\, dx$

Answer

23. Which of the following are properties of the definite integral?

 I. $\displaystyle\int_a^b k f(x)\, dx = k \int_a^b f(x)\, dx,\ k \neq 0$

 II. $\displaystyle\int_a^b x f(x)\, dx = x \int_a^b f(x)\, dx$

 III. $\displaystyle\int_a^b f(x)\, dx = \int_a^c f(x)\, dx + \int_c^b f(x)\, dx$

(A) I only

(B) I and III only

(C) II and III only

(D) I, II, and III

Answer

24. If $f(x) = \sqrt{e^{2x} + 1}$, then $f'(0) =$

(A) $\dfrac{\sqrt{2}}{4}$ (B) $\dfrac{\sqrt{2}}{2}$ (C) 1 (D) $\sqrt{2}$

Answer

25. If $\lim\limits_{x \to a} \dfrac{\tan^{-1}(2x) - \tan^{-1}(2a)}{x - a} = \dfrac{2}{3}$, then a could equal

(A) $\sqrt{2}$ (B) 1 (C) $\dfrac{\sqrt{2}}{2}$ (D) $\dfrac{\sqrt{2}}{4}$

$$\tan^{-1} x = \frac{1}{1+x^2}$$

Answer

26. The base of a solid is the region in the first quadrant bounded by the line $x + 2y = 4$ and the coordinate axes. What is the volume of the solid if every cross section perpendicular to the x-axis is a semicircle?

(A) $\dfrac{2\pi}{3}$ (B) $\dfrac{4\pi}{3}$ (C) $\dfrac{8\pi}{3}$ (D) $\dfrac{16\pi}{3}$

Answer

27. $\displaystyle\sum_{n=1}^{\infty} \sin\left(\dfrac{1}{n}\right)$ will

(A) converge by the nth term test.

(B) converge by the Alternating Series Test.

(C) diverge by the Ratio Test.

(D) diverge by the Limit Comparison Test.

Answer

28. The current number of bacteria in a culture is 9,000 and is increasing at the rate of $2700e^{0.3t}$ per hour. What will be the number of bacteria present in the culture in 5 hours?

(A) $2700e^{1.5}$ (B) $2700e^3$ (C) $9000e^{1.5}$ (D) $9000e^3$

Answer

29. The average value of a continuous function $f(x)$ on the closed interval $[3,7]$ is 12. What is the value of $\int_3^7 f(x)\, dx$?

(A) 4   (B) 12   (C) 24   (D) 48

Answer

30. Let $y(x)$ be the solution to the differentiable equation $\dfrac{dy}{dx} = y^2 - xy$ with the initial condition $y(2) = 3$. What is the approximation for $y(3)$ obtained by using Euler's Method with two steps starting with $x = 2$?

(A) 0   (B) 4.5   (C) 6   (D) 9

Answer

SECTION I PART B

Directions: Solve each of the following problems, using available space for scratch work. After examining the form of the choices, decide which is the best of the choices given. Do not spend too much time on any one problem.

In this exam:

(1) The exact numerical value of the correct answer does not always appear among the choices given. When this happens, select from among the choices the number that best approximates the exact numerical value.

(2) Unless otherwise specified, the domain of a function f is assumed to be the set of all real numbers x for which $f(x)$ is a real number.

(3) The inverse of a trigonometric function f may be indicated using the inverse function notation f^{-1} or with the prefix "arc" (e.g., $\sin^{-1}x = \arcsin x$)

31. Consider the series $\sum_{n=1}^{\infty} \dfrac{2^n}{(n+1)!}$. If the Ratio Test is applied to this series, which of the following inequalities indicates that the series is convergent?

(A) $\displaystyle\lim_{n \to \infty} \dfrac{2}{n+2} < 1$

(B) $\displaystyle\lim_{n \to \infty} \dfrac{n+2}{2} < 1$

(C) $\displaystyle\lim_{n \to \infty} \dfrac{2^n}{n+2} < 1$

(D) $\displaystyle\lim_{n \to \infty} \dfrac{2^n}{(n+2)!} < 1$

Answer

32. If n is a positive integer, the function $f(x) = x^2 + 5 \cos x$ will have how many points of inflection over the interval $[0, 2\pi n]$?

(A) 2   (B) 2π (C) n (D) $2n$

Answer

33. If $y^2 - 2xy = 21$, then $\dfrac{dy}{dx}$ at the point $(2, -3)$ is

(A) $\dfrac{6}{5}$ (B) $\dfrac{3}{5}$ (C) $-\dfrac{2}{5}$ (D) $-\dfrac{3}{5}$

Answer

34. Let f be the function given by $f(x) = \displaystyle\int_0^{2x} \cos(t^2)\, dt$, $x \geq 0$.

The fifth-degree Taylor polynomial approximation of f about $x = 0$ is

(A) $2x - 16x^5$

(B) $2x - \dfrac{x^5}{5}$

(C) $2x - \dfrac{32x^5}{5}$

(D) $2x - \dfrac{16x^5}{5}$

Answer

35. A particle moves in the xy-plane so that its position at any time t is given by $x(t) = 4\sin(\pi t)$ and $y(t) = (3t-1)^2$. What is the speed of the particle when $t = 2$?

    (A) 13.708   (B) 30.209   (C) 32.526   (D) 42.566

Answer

36. The second derivative of a function is given by $f''(x) = 0.5 + \cos(x) - e^{-x}$. Over the interval $[-2,4]$ the graph of function f changes from concave up to concave down at approximately $x =$

    (A) −0.36   (B) 0.59   (C) 1.93   (D) 3.10

Answer

37. A particle moving along a curve in the xy-plane has a position vector given by $\left\langle \frac{t^4}{4}, \sin(t) \right\rangle$. What is the total distance the particle travels between $t = 0$ and $t = \pi$?

(A) 25.7   (B) 25.1   (C) 7.6   (D) 7.7

Answer

38. Let f be a function that is everywhere differentiable. The table below provides information about $f(x)$ and its first, second, and third derivatives for selected values of x.

x	$f(x)$	$f'(x)$	$f''(x)$	$f'''(x)$
0	4	2	1	0.50
1	5.15	2.50	1.25	0.75
2	7.20	3.50	1.75	0.85
3	10.50	5.25	2.10	1.00

Which of the following best approximates $f(2.2)$?

(A) $4 + 2(0.2) + \dfrac{1(0.2)^2}{2} + \dfrac{0.5}{6}(0.2)^3$

(B) $4 + 2(2.2) + \dfrac{1}{2}(2.2)^2 + \dfrac{0.50}{6}(2.2)^3$

(C) $7.20 + 3.50(2.2) + \dfrac{1.75}{2}(2.2)^2 + \dfrac{0.85}{6}(2.2)^3$

(D) $7.20 + 3.50(0.2) + \dfrac{1.75}{2}(0.2)^2 + \dfrac{0.85}{6}(0.2)^3$

Answer

39. Let E be the error when the Taylor polynomial $T(x) = x - \dfrac{x^3}{3!}$, centered about $x = 0$, is used to approximate $f(x) = \sin x$ at $x = 0.5$. Which of the following is true?

(A) $0.0001 < |E| < 0.0003$

(B) $0.0003 < |E| < 0.0005$

(C) $0.0005 < |E| < 0.0007$

(D) $0.0007 < |E|$

Answer

40. If $\displaystyle\int_2^x f(t)\, dt = \dfrac{6x}{\sqrt{9x^2 - 20}} - 3$, then $\displaystyle\int_2^\infty f(t)\, dt$ is

(A) -3 (B) -1 (C) 0 (D) divergent

Answer

41. Let $f(x) = x^3 - 7x^2 + 25x - 39$ and let g be the inverse function of f. What is the value of $g'(0)$?

(A) $\frac{1}{25}$　　(B) $\frac{1}{10}$　　(C) 10　　(D) 25

Answer

42. Oil flows into a concrete conical storage pit at the rate of 10 cubic feet per minute. The pit was built point down and has a depth of 15 feet and a ground level radius of 9 feet. How fast, in feet per minute, is the oil level rising when the oil is 10 feet deep?

(A) 0.05　　(B) 0.09　　(C) 0.13　　(D) 0.44

Answer

$$f(x) = \begin{cases} e^{-x} + 2 & \text{for } x < 0 \\ ax + b & \text{for } x \geq 0 \end{cases}$$

43. Let f be the function defined above, where a and b are constants. If f is differentiable at $x = 0$, what is the value of $a + b$?

(A) -2 (B) 0   (C) 2   (D) 4

Answer

44. Let f be a function whose derivative is given by $f'(x) = \frac{x}{15} + \sin(e^{0.2x})$. Which of the following is the approximate x-value of a relative maximum point on the graph of f ?

(A) 2.830

(B) 6.378

(C) 8.673

(D) 10.332

Answer

45. What is the interval of convergence of the series $\displaystyle\sum_{n=1}^{\infty} \frac{(x-2)^n}{3^n(n+1)}$?

(A) $-1 \le x < 5$

(B) $-1 < x \le 5$

(C) $-1 \le x \le 5$

(D) $-1 < x < 5$

Answer

NO TESTING MATERIAL ON THIS PAGE

FREE-RESPONSE QUESTIONS — GENERAL INSTRUCTIONS

For each part of Section II, you may wish to look over the problems before starting to work on them. It is not expected that everyone will be able to complete all parts of all problems. All problems are given equal weight, but the parts of a particular problem are not necessarily given equal weight.

YOU SHOULD WRITE ALL WORK FOR EACH PART OF EACH PROBLEM IN THE SPACE PROVIDED FOR THAT PART. Be sure to write clearly and legibly. If you make an error, you may save time by crossing it out rather than trying to erase it. Erased or crossed-out work will not be graded. Manage your time carefully.

- Show all your work, even though a question may not explicitly remind you to do so. Clearly label any functions, graphs, tables, or other objects that you use. Your work will be graded on the correctness and completeness of your methods as well as your answers. Answers without supporting work will usually not receive credit.

- Justifications require that you give mathematical (noncalculator) reasons.

- Your work must be expressed in standard mathematical notation rather than calculator syntax. For example, $\int_1^5 x^2\,dx$ may not be written as fnInt(X^2, X, 1, 5).

- Unless otherwise specified, answers (numeric or algebraic) need not be simplified.

- If you use decimal approximations in calculations, your work will be graded on accuracy. Unless otherwise specified, your final answers should be accurate to three places after the decimal point.

- Unless otherwise specified, the domain of a function f is assumed to be the set of all real numbers x for which $f(x)$ is a real number.

SECTION II PART A: 30 Minutes, Questions 1,2

A graphing calculator is required.

During the timed portion for Part A, you may work only on the problems in Part A. Write your solution to each part of each problem in the space provided.

On Part A, you are permitted to use your calculator to solve an equation, find the derivative of a function at a point, or calculate the value of a definite integral. However, you must clearly indicate the setup of your programs, you must show the mathematical steps necessary to produce your results.

Do not go on to Part B until you are told to do so.

SECTION II PART B: 60 Minutes, Questions 3,4,5,6

Write your solution to each part of each problem in the space provided for that part. During the timed portion for Part B, you may continue to work on the problems in Part A without the use of any calculator.

Section II Part A: A graphing calculator is required for these problems.

1. A particle moves along the x-axis so that at any time t, $0.1 < t < 0.3$, its velocity is given by $v(t) = \sin\left(\frac{1}{t}\right)$.

   (a) Find an expression for the acceleration of the particle at any time t in the given interval.
   (b) When is the velocity the greatest? Use part (a) to justify your answer.
   (c) If the position of the particle, $x(t)$, at $t = 0.16$ is 0, find the position of the particle at $t = 0.25$. Show your work that leads to your answer.
   (d) During the given interval, does the particle spend more time moving to the left or to the right? Justify your answer.

   (a) Find an expression for the acceleration of the particle at any time t in the given interval.

   (b) When is the velocity the greatest? Use part (a) to justify your answer.

(c)   If the position of the particle, $x(t)$, at $t = 0.16$ is 0, find the position of the particle at $t = 0.25$. Show your work that leads to your answer.

(d)   During the given interval, does the particle spend more time moving to the left or to the right? Justify your answer.

2. Sand is being poured into a bin that is initially empty. During the work day, for $0 \leq t \leq 9$ hours, the sand pours into the bin at the rate given by

$$S(t) = \frac{5000}{t^3 + 50} \text{ cubic meters per hour.}$$

After one hour, for $1 \leq t \leq 9$, sand is removed from the bin at the rate of

$$R(t) = 23.9665 \sqrt{t} \text{ cubic meters per hour.}$$

(a) How much sand is poured into the bin during the work day? Include units of measure.
(b) Find $S(6) - R(6)$ and include units of measure. Explain what this amount means in the context of the problem.
(c) Explain why the amount of sand in the bin is at a maximum when $S(t) = R(t)$.
(d) How much sand, in cubic meters, is in the bin at the end of the work day?

(a) How much sand is poured into the bin during the work day? Include units of measure.

(b) Find $S(6) - R(6)$ and include units of measure. Explain what this amount means in the context of the problem.

(c) Explain why the amount of sand in the bin is at a maximum when $S(t) = R(t)$.

(d) How much sand, in cubic meters, is in the bin at the end of the work day?

Section II Part B: No calculator is allowed for these problems.

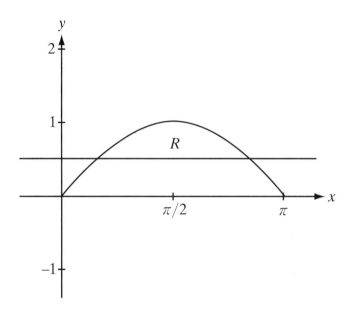

3. Let R be the region bounded by the graphs of $y = \sin(x)$ and $y = \frac{1}{2}$ as shown in the figure above.

(a) Find the area of R.

(b) Write, but do not evaluate, an integral expression that gives the volume of the solid generated when R is revolved around the x-axis.

(c) The region R is the base of a solid. For each x in region R, the cross sections of this solid, perpendicular to the x-axis, are semicircles. Write, but do not evaluate, an integral expression that gives the volume of the solid.

(a) Find the area of R.

(b)   Write, but do not evaluate, an integral expression that gives the volume of the solid generated when R is revolved around the x-axis.

(c)   The region R is the base of a solid. For each x in region R, the cross sections of this solid, perpendicular to the x-axis, are semicircles. Write, but do not evaluate, an integral expression that gives the volume of the solid.

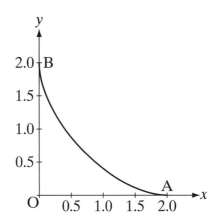

4. Let the coordinate axes represent two highways that meet at right angles. In order to safely connect the two highways, a curved road is to be built from point A to point B as shown in the figure above. The parametric equations of the connecting road are

$$x(t) = 2\cos^3 t \text{ and } y(t) = 2\sin^3 t \text{ for } 0 \le t \le \frac{\pi}{2}, \text{ where } x(t) \text{ and } y(t) \text{ are in miles.}$$

In order to make the intersections safe, the slope of the curved road should be the same as the slope of each highway where they meet.

(a) Find $\dfrac{dy}{dx}$ in terms of t.

(b) Show that the slope of the curved road and the slope of each highway are the same at points A and B.

(c) Set up but do not evaluate an integral expression which gives the length of the curved road from A to B.

(a) Find $\dfrac{dy}{dx}$ in terms of t.

(b)   Show that the slope of the curved road and the slope of each highway are the same at points A and B.

(c)   Set up but do not evaluate an integral expression which gives the length of the curved road from A to B.

5. Let $f(x)$ be the function defined by the power series

$$1 - \frac{1}{3}(x-2) + \frac{1}{9}(x-2)^2 - \frac{1}{27}(x-2)^3 + \cdots + (-1)^n \frac{(x-2)^n}{3^n} + \cdots$$

(a) For what values of x does the series converge?
(b) Write the first four non-zero terms and the general term of the power series for $f'(x)$ centered at $x = 2$ and find $f'(2)$.
(c) Write an equation of the tangent line of $f(x)$ at the point where $x = 2$.
(d) Near $x = 2$, does the tangent line lie above the curve or below the curve? Justify your answer.

(a) For what values of x does the series converge?

(b) Write the first four non-zero terms and the general term of the power series for $f'(x)$ centered at $x = 2$ and find $f'(2)$.

(c)   Write an equation of the tangent line of $f(x)$ at the point where $x = 2$.

(d)   Near $x = 2$, does the tangent line lie above the curve or below the curve? Justify your answer.

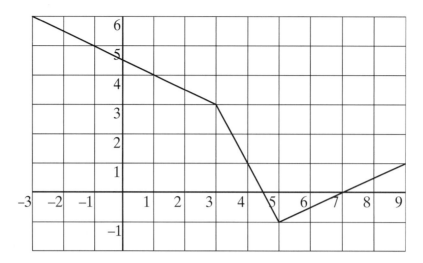

The graph of f

6. Let f be a function defined on the closed interval $[-3,9]$. The graph of f, consisting of three line segments is shown above. Let $g(x) = \int_0^x f(t)\, dt$.

   (a) Find $g(4.5)$, $g'(4.5)$, and $g''(4.5)$.
   (b) Find the average value of f on the closed interval $[-3,5]$. Show the work that leads to your answer.
   (c) Find the x-coordinate of any points of inflection of g. Justify your answer.
   (d) Find the coordinates of all maximum points of g.

   (a) Find $g(4.5)$, $g'(4.5)$, and $g''(4.5)$.

(b)   Find the average value of *f* on the closed interval $[-3,5]$. Show the work that leads to your answer.

(c)   Find the *x*-coordinate of any points of inflection of *g*. Justify your answer.

(d)   Find the coordinates of all maximum points of *g*.

SAMPLE EXAMINATION IV
SECTION I PART A

NO CALCULATOR IS ALLOWED IN THIS SECTION.

Directions: Solve each of the following problems, using the available space for scratch work. After examining the form of the choices, decide which is the best of the choices given. Do not spend too much time on any one problem.

In this exam:

(1) Unless otherwise specified, the domain of a function f is assumed to be the set of all real numbers x for which $f(x)$ is a real number.

(2) The inverse of a trigonometric function f may be indicated using the inverse function notation f^{-1} or with the prefix "arc" (e.g., $\sin^{-1} x = \arcsin x$)

1. If f is continuous for all real numbers, $\dfrac{dy}{dx} = f(x)$ and $y(2) = 4$, then $y(x) =$

(A) $4 + \displaystyle\int_2^x f'(t)\,dt$

(B) $4 + \displaystyle\int_2^x f(t)\,dt$

(C) $\displaystyle\int_2^x f(t)\,dt - 4$

(D) $4 - \displaystyle\int_2^x f(t)\,dt$

$$y(x) - y(\ ) = \int_2^x f'(t)\,dt \quad +4$$

Answer

A

2. For what value(s) of x does $4x^6 - 8x^3 + 18$ have a relative minimum?

(A) -1 only

(B) 0 only

(C) 1 only

(D) 0 and 1 only

$24x^5 - 24x^2$

$24x^2\left(x^3 - 1\right)$

$24x^5 - 24x^2$

$24x^2\left(x^3 - 1\right) = 0$

$\cancel{24x^2 = 0}$ $\qquad (x^3 - 1) = 0$

$\cancel{x = 0}$ $\qquad x = 1$

Answer

A

3. A curve is given parametrically by the equations $x = 3 - 4\sin t$ and $y = 4 + 3\cos t$ for $0 \le t \le 2\pi$. What are all points (x,y) at which the curve has a vertical tangent?

(A) $(-1,4)$

(B) $(3,7)$

(C) $(-1,4)$ and $(7,4)$

(D) $(3,7)$ and $(3,1)$

Answer

C

4. The average value of $\sqrt{3x}$ on the closed interval $[0,9]$ is

(A) $\dfrac{2\sqrt{3}}{3}$ (B) $2\sqrt{3}$ (C) 6 (D) $6\sqrt{3}$

$$\frac{\displaystyle\int_0^9 \sqrt{3x}\ dx}{9}$$

$$= \frac{\dfrac{2}{3}(3x)^{3/2}\Big|_0^9}{9}$$

$$= \frac{\dfrac{2}{3}\sqrt{(27)^3}}{9}$$

Answer

D

5. What are all values of x for which $\displaystyle\sum_{n=1}^{\infty} \frac{2^n x^n}{n}$ converges?

(A) $-\dfrac{1}{2} \le x \le \dfrac{1}{2}$

(B) $-\dfrac{1}{2} < x < \dfrac{1}{2}$

(C) $-\dfrac{1}{2} < x \le \dfrac{1}{2}$

(D) $-\dfrac{1}{2} \le x < \dfrac{1}{2}$

Answer

6. The position of a particle on the x-axis at time t, $t > 0$, is $\ln t$. The average velocity of the particle for $1 \le t \le e$ is

(A) $\dfrac{1}{e} - 1$ 　　(B) $\dfrac{1}{e-1}$ 　　(C) e 　　(D) $e - 1$

-1.09

$$\frac{\displaystyle\int_1^e \text{lnt} \ dt}{e-1}$$

$\dfrac{1-e}{e} \cdot (e-1)$

Answer

B

7. As a particle moves along the polar curve $r = \tan(2\theta)$ at what rate is its distance to the origin changing when $\theta = \frac{\pi}{6}$?

(A) 8   (B) 4   (C) $\frac{8}{3}$ (D) $\frac{4}{3}$

Answer

8. An antiderivative of $2x\cos(2x)$ is

(A) $2x\cos(2x) - 2\sin(2x)$

(B) $x\sin(2x) - \frac{1}{2}\cos 2(x)$

(C) $2x\sin(2x) + 2\cos(2x)$

(D) $x\sin(2x) + \frac{1}{2}\cos(2x)$

2 anti of cos is sin

+ sin (2x)´

2x cos (2x)

Answer

9. $\displaystyle\int_{-3}^{3} |x+2|\, dx =$

(A) 0   (B) 8   (C) 13   (D) 21

Answer

10. Let R be the region in the <u>fourth quadrant</u> enclosed by the x-axis and the curve $y = x^2 - 2kx$, where k is a constant. If the area of the region R is 36, then the value of k is

(A) −3   (B) 3   (C) 4   (D) 6

Answer

11. $\lim\limits_{h \to 0} \dfrac{1}{h} \displaystyle\int_0^h \dfrac{\sin^2 t}{t^2}\, dt$ is

(A) 0   (B) $\dfrac{1}{2}$ (C) 1   (D) nonexistent

Answer

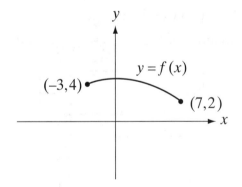

12. The graph of $y = f(x)$ on the closed interval $[-3,7]$ is shown in the figure above. If f is continuous on $[-3,7]$ and differentiable on $(-3,7)$, then there exists a c, $-3 < c < 7$, such that

(A) $f'(c)$ is undefined.

(B) $f'(c) = \dfrac{1}{5}$

(C) $f'(c) = -\dfrac{1}{5}$

(D) $f'(c) = -5$

Answer

x	1	2	3	4	5	6
$g(x)$	0	1	3	7	2	5
$g'(x)$	4	3	1	-1	-2	-1

13. Let $f(x) = x^2 + 3x$ and let $g(x)$ and its derivative $g'(x)$ have the values shown in the table above. If $h(x) = f(g(x))$, what is $h'(2)$?

(A) 5   (B) 10   (C) 15   (D) 21

Answer

14. Let $f(x)$ be a differentiable function. The table below gives the value of $f(x)$ and $f'(x)$, the derivative of $f(x)$, at selected values of x. If $g(x) = \dfrac{1}{f(x)}$, what is the value of $g'(2)$?

x	1	2	3	4
$f(x)$	-3	-8	-9	0
$f'(x)$	-5	-4	3	16

(A) $-\dfrac{1}{8}$ (B) $\dfrac{1}{16}$ (C) $\dfrac{1}{64}$ (D) 16

Answer

15. Which of the following series converge?

$$\text{I.} \quad \sum_{n=1}^{\infty}\left(1-\frac{4}{3}\right)^{n}$$

$$\text{II.} \quad \sum_{n=1}^{\infty}\left(1+\frac{4}{3}\right)^{n}$$

$$\text{III.} \quad \sum_{n=1}^{\infty}\left(1+\frac{1}{n}\right)^{n}$$

(A) I only

(B) III only

(C) I and II only

(D) I and III only

Answer

16. What is the 20th derivative of $y = \sin(2x)$?

(A) $-2^{20}\sin(2x)$

(B) $2^{20}\sin(2x)$

(C) $-2^{20}\cos(2x)$

(D) $2^{20}\cos(2x)$

Answer

17. If $f(x) = 15 - g(x)$ for $-2 \leq x \leq 2$, then $\int_{-2}^{2} [f(x) - g(x)] \, dx =$

(A) $2\int_{-2}^{2} g(x) \, dx - 60$

(B) $2\int_{-2}^{2} g(x) \, dx + 60$

(C) $60 - 4\int_{0}^{2} g(x) \, dx$

(D) $60 - 2\int_{-2}^{2} g(x) \, dx$

Answer

18. A forest is in the shape of a rectangle 5 miles long and 3 miles wide. The density of trees at a distance of x miles from the 5-mile side is given by $\rho(x)$ trees per square mile. Which expression gives the number of trees in the forest?

(A) $3\int_{0}^{3} \rho(x) \, dx$

(B) $5\int_{0}^{3} \rho(x) \, dx$

(C) $3\int_{0}^{3} \rho'(x) \, dx$

(D) $5\int_{0}^{3} \rho'(x) \, dx$

Answer

19. An equation of the line tangent to the curve $x^2 + y^2 = 169$ at the point $(5, -12)$ is

(A) $12x - 5y = 119$

(B) $5x - 12y = 119$

(C) $5x - 12y = 169$

(D) $12x - 5y = 169$

Answer

20. Let $f(x) = \begin{cases} 1 + e^{-x} & \text{for } 0 \le x \le 5 \\ 1 + e^{x-10} & \text{for } 5 < x \le 10 \end{cases}$

Which of the following statements are true?

I. $f(x)$ is continuous for all values of x in the interval $[0,10]$.

II. $f'(x)$, the derivative of $f(x)$, is continuous for all values of x in the interval $[0,10]$.

III. The graph of $f(x)$ is concave upwards for all values of x in the interval $[0,10]$.

(A) I and II only

(B) II and III only

(C) I and III only

(D) I, II, and III

Answer

21. A solid has a circular base of radius 3. If every plane cross section perpendicular to the *x*-axis is an equilateral triangle, then its volume is

(A) $12\sqrt{3}$ (B) $18\sqrt{3}$ (C) $24\sqrt{3}$ (D) $36\sqrt{3}$

Answer

22. The rate of change of the velocity of a particle moving on the *x*-axis is given by the function $R(t) = -\sin(t) - \sqrt{3}\cos(t)$, for $t \geq 0$. At $t = 0$, the velocity of the particle is 1.

At $t = 0$, which statement is true?

(A)   The particle is moving to the right and its speed is decreasing.

(B)   The particle is moving to the left and its speed is decreasing.

(C)   The particle is moving to the right and its speed is increasing.

(D)   The particle is moving to the left and its speed is increasing.

Answer

23. If $s_n = \left(\dfrac{(8-n)^{200}}{8^{n+2}} \right) \left(\dfrac{8^n}{(3-n^2)^{100}} \right)$, to what number does the sequence $\{s_n\}$ converge as $n \to \infty$?

(A) $-\dfrac{1}{8}$ (B) $-\dfrac{1}{64}$ (C) $\dfrac{1}{64}$ (D) $\dfrac{1}{8}$

Answer

24. If $y = \sin^{-1}\left(\dfrac{3x}{4} \right)$, then $\dfrac{dy}{dx} =$

(A) $\dfrac{3}{\sqrt{16 + 9x^2}}$

(B) $\dfrac{3}{\sqrt{16 - 9x^2}}$

(C) $\dfrac{4}{\sqrt{16 - 9x^2}}$

(D) $\dfrac{12}{\sqrt{16 + 9x^2}}$

Answer

25. What are the horizontal asymptotes of all of the solutions of the logistic differential equation $\frac{dy}{dx} = y\left(8 - \frac{y}{1,000}\right)$?

(A) $y = 0$ only

(B) $y = 8$ only

(C) $y = 0$ and $y = 8$

(D) $y = 0$ and $y = 8,000$

Answer

26. $\int_0^4 \frac{x}{x^2 - 4} dx$ is

(A) 0   (B) $\ln\left(\sqrt{3}\right)$ (C) $\ln(3)$ (D) divergent

Answer

27. The slope field for the differential equation $\dfrac{dy}{dx} = f(x)$ is shown below for $-4 < x < 4$ and $-4 < y < 4$. Which of the following statements is true for all possible solutions of the differential equation?

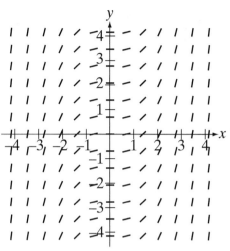

    I. For $x < 0$, all solution functions are decreasing.

    II. For $x > 0$, all solution functions are increasing.

    III. All solution functions level off near the y-axis.

(A) I and II only

(B) II and III only

(C) I and III only

(D) I, II, and III

Answer

28. At which of the three points on the graph of $y = f(x)$ in the figure below will $f'(x) < f''(x)$?

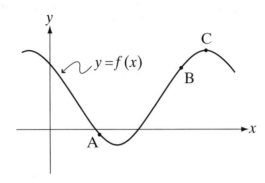

(A) A only

(B) C only

(C) A and B only

(D) A and C only

Answer

29. A particle with velocity at any time t given by $v(t) = 2e^{2t}$ moves in a straight line. How far does the particle travel during the time interval when its velocity increases from 2 to 4?

(A) 1   (B) 2   (C) 3   (D) e^4

Answer

30. If the derivative of a function f is given by $f'(x) = \frac{1}{5}(x^2 - 4)^5 - x^2$, how many points of inflection will the graph of function f have?

(A) 2   (B) 3   (C) 4   (D) 5

Answer

SECTION I PART B

A GRAPHING CALCULATOR IS REQUIRED FOR SOME QUESTIONS IN THIS SECTION.

Directions: Solve each of the following problems, using available space for scratch work. After examining the form of the choices, decide which is the best of the choices given. Do not spend too much time on any one problem.

In this exam:

   (1)   The exact numerical value of the correct answer does not always appear among the choices given. When this happens, select from among the choices the number that best approximates the exact numerical value.

   (2)   Unless otherwise specified, the domain of a function f is assumed to be the set of all real numbers x for which $f(x)$ is a real number.

   (3)   The inverse of a trigonometric function f may be indicated using the inverse function notation f^{-1} or with the prefix "arc" (e.g., $\sin^{-1}x = \arcsin x$)

x	0	2	4	6
$f(x)$	5	3	1	2
$f'(x)$	−3	−2	0	2

31. Selected values of a differentiable function f and its first derivative are given in the table above. Using a trapezoidal sum with three subintervals of equal length, which of the following is an approximation of the length of the graph of f over the closed interval $[0,6]$?

(A) 15

(B) $\sqrt{7} + 3\sqrt{5} + 2$

(C) $\sqrt{10} + 3\sqrt{5} + 2$

(D) $\sqrt{26} + 2\sqrt{10} + 2\sqrt{3} + \sqrt{5}$

Answer

32. What is an equation of the line tangent to the graph of $f(x) = 7x - x^2$ at the point where $f'(x) = 3$?

(A) $y = 3x + 4$

(B) $y = 3x + 8$

(C) $y = 3x - 10$

(D) $y = 3x - 16$

Answer

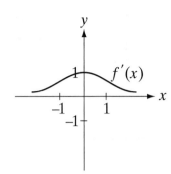

33. Suppose the derivative of f has the graph shown above.

Which of the following could be the graph of f?

(A)

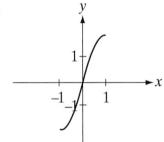

(B)

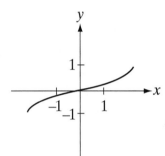

(C)

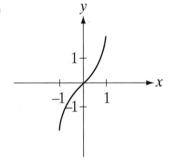

(D)

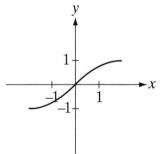

Answer

34. The velocity vector of a particle moving in the xy-plane is given by $v(t) = \langle 2 \sin t, 3 \cos t \rangle$ for $t \geq 0$. At $t = 0$, the particle is at the point $(1,1)$. What is the position vector at $t = 2$?

   (A) $\langle 3.832, 3.728 \rangle$

   (B) $\langle 1.832, -1.728 \rangle$

   (C) $\langle 1.819, -1.248 \rangle$

   (D) $\langle 1.735, -0.532 \rangle$

Answer

35. Let f be the function given by $f(t) = \int_0^t e^{x \cos(x)} \left(\cos(x) - x \sin(x) \right) dx, 0 \leq t \leq 10$. At which of the following values of t does f attain its absolute maximum value?

   (A) 0.860

   (B) 3.426

   (C) 6.437

   (D) 9.529

Answer

36. The length of the curve $y = x^3$ from $(0,0)$ to $(1,1)$ is

(A) 1.732   (B) 1.548   (C) 1.414   (D) 1.404

Answer

37. If $\dfrac{dy}{dt} = \dfrac{2y}{t(t+2)}$ for $t > 0$ and $y = 1$ when $t = 1$, then when $t = 2$, $y =$

(A) $\dfrac{1}{2}$ (B) $\dfrac{2}{3}$ (C) 1   (D) $\dfrac{3}{2}$

Answer

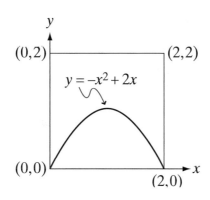

38. As shown in the figure above, a square with vertices $(0,0)$, $(2,0)$, $(2,2)$, and $(0,2)$ is divided into two regions by the graph of $y = -x^2 + 2x$. If a point is picked at random from inside the square, what is the probability that the point lies in the region above the parabola?

(A) $\dfrac{3}{4}$　　　(B) $\dfrac{2}{3}$　　　(C) $\dfrac{5}{8}$　　　(D) $\dfrac{3}{5}$

Answer

39. Let $f(x)$ be a function that is differentiable for all x. The derivative of this function is given by the power series

$$f'(x) = 3x - \frac{9x^3}{2} + \frac{81x^5}{40} - \frac{3x^7}{60} + \cdots$$

If $f(0) = 2$, then $f(x) =$

(A) $2 + 3x - \dfrac{9x^3}{2} + \dfrac{81x^5}{40} - \dfrac{3x^7}{60} + \cdots$

(B) $\dfrac{3x^2}{2} - \dfrac{9x^4}{8} + \dfrac{27x^6}{80} - \dfrac{3x^8}{480} + \cdots$

(C) $2 - \dfrac{3x^2}{2} + \dfrac{9x^4}{8} - \dfrac{27x^6}{80} + \dfrac{3x^8}{480} + \cdots$

(D) $2 + \dfrac{3x^2}{2} - \dfrac{9x^4}{8} + \dfrac{27x^6}{80} - \dfrac{3x^8}{480} + \cdots$

Answer

40. As $h \to 0$, let f be a differentiable function such that for all x, $f(x+h) - f(x) = 6xh + 4h^2$. If $f(2) = 5$, what is the value of $f(1)$?

(A) -4

(B) -1

(C) 3

(D) 10

Answer

41. The circumference of a circle is increasing at the rate of 0.5 meters/minute. What is the rate of change of the area of the circle when the radius is 4 meters?

(A) $8\pi \, \text{m}^2/\text{min}$

(B) $4\pi \, \text{m}^2/\text{min}$

(C) $4 \, \text{m}^2/\text{min}$

(D) $2 \, \text{m}^2/\text{min}$

Answer

42. Let g be the function defined by $g(x) = \int_{3}^{x} ((5 + 4t - t^2)(2^{-t}))\, dt$. Which of the following statements about g must be true?

      I. g is increasing on $(3,5)$.

      II. g is increasing on $(5,7)$.

      III. $g(7) < 0$

(A) I only

(B) III only

(C) I and III only

(D) I, II, and III

Answer

43. A region R is enclosed by the coordinate axes and the graph of $y = k(x - 5)^2, k > 0$. When this region is revolved around the x-axis, the solid formed has a volume of 2500π cubic units. What is the value of k?

(A) $2\sqrt{15}$ (B) 4   (C) $\sqrt{5}$ (D) 2

Answer

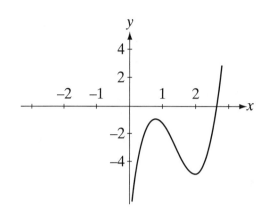

44. The graph above shows a function f with a relative minimum at $x = 2$. The approximation of $f(x)$ near $x = 2$ using a second-degree Taylor polynomial centered about $x = 2$ is given by $a + b(x - 2) + c(x - 2)^2$.

Which of the following is true about a, b, and c ?

(A) $a < 0, b = 0, c > 0$

(B) $a > 0, b = 0, c < 0$

(C) $a < 0, b > 0, c > 0$

(D) $a > 0, b = 0, c > 0$

Answer

45. The solution of the differential equation $\frac{dy}{dx} = -\frac{x^2}{y}$ contains the point $(3, -2)$. Using Euler's Method with $\Delta x = -0.3$, what is the approximate value of y when $x = 2.7$?

(A) -2.98

(B) -3.08

(C) -3.25

(D) -3.35

Answer

FREE-RESPONSE QUESTIONS — GENERAL INSTRUCTIONS

For each part of Section II, you may wish to look over the problems before starting to work on them. It is not expected that everyone will be able to complete all parts of all problems. All problems are given equal weight, but the parts of a particular problem are not necessarily given equal weight.

YOU SHOULD WRITE ALL WORK FOR EACH PART OF EACH PROBLEM IN THE SPACE PROVIDED FOR THAT PART. Be sure to write clearly and legibly. If you make an error, you may save time by crossing it out rather than trying to erase it. Erased or crossed-out work will not be graded. Manage your time carefully.

- Show all your work, even though a question may not explicitly remind you to do so. Clearly label any functions, graphs, tables, or other objects that you use. Your work will be graded on the correctness and completeness of your methods as well as your answers. Answers without supporting work will usually not receive credit.

- Justifications require that you give mathematical (noncalculator) reasons.

- Your work must be expressed in standard mathematical notation rather than calculator syntax. For example, $\int_1^5 x^2\,dx$ may not be written as fnInt(X^2, X, 1, 5).

- Unless otherwise specified, answers (numeric or algebraic) need not be simplified.

- If you use decimal approximations in calculations, your work will be graded on accuracy. Unless otherwise specified, your final answers should be accurate to three places after the decimal point.

- Unless otherwise specified, the domain of a function f is assumed to be the set of all real numbers x for which $f(x)$ is a real number.

SECTION II PART A: 30 Minutes, Questions 1,2

A graphing calculator is required.

During the timed portion for Part A, you may work only on the problems in Part A. Write your solution to each part of each problem in the space provided.

On Part A, you are permitted to use your calculator to solve an equation, find the derivative of a function at a point, or calculate the value of a definite integral. However, you must clearly indicate the setup of your programs, you must show the mathematical steps necessary to produce your results.

Do not go on to Part B until you are told to do so.

SECTION II PART B: 60 Minutes, Questions 3,4,5,6

Write your solution to each part of each problem in the space provided for that part. During the timed portion for Part B, you may continue to work on the problems in Part A without the use of any calculator.

Section II Part A: A graphing calculator is required for these problems.

1. Let f be the function given by $f(x) = \dfrac{1}{\sqrt{2\pi}} e^{-x^2/2}$ for all real numbers x.

 (a) Find $\lim_{x \to -\infty} f(x)$ and $\lim_{x \to \infty} f(x)$.

 (b) Find $f'(3)$.

 (c) Find the x-coordinates of the points of inflection.

 (d) Find the area of the region enclosed by the x-axis, the graph of f and the vertical lines containing the points of inflection found in part (c).

 (a) Find $\lim_{x \to -\infty} f(x)$ and $\lim_{x \to \infty} f(x)$.

 (b) Find $f'(3)$.

(c)   Find the x-coordinates of the points of inflection.

(d)   Find the area of the region enclosed by the x-axis, the graph of f and the vertical lines containing the points of inflection found in part (c).

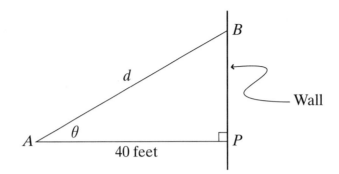

2. As shown in the figure above, a searchlight is located at point A, 40 feet from a wall. The searchlight revolves counterclockwise at a rate of $\frac{\pi}{30}$ radians per second. At any point B on the wall, the strength of the light L, is inversely proportional to the square of the distance d from A; that is, at any point on the wall $L = \frac{k}{d^2}$. At the closest point P, $L = 10{,}000$ lumens.

(a)   Find the constant of proportionality k.
(b)   Express L as a function of θ, the angle formed by $\overline{AP}$ and $\overline{AB}$.
(c)   How fast (in lumens/second) is the strength of the light changing when $\theta = \frac{\pi}{4}$? Is it increasing or decreasing? Justify your answer.

(a)   Find the constant of proportionality k.

(b)   Express L as a function of θ, the angle formed by $\overline{AP}$ and $\overline{AB}$.

(c)   How fast (in lumens/second) is the strength of the light changing when $\theta = \frac{\pi}{4}$? Is it increasing or decreasing? Justify your answer.

Section II Part B: No calculator is allowed for these problems.

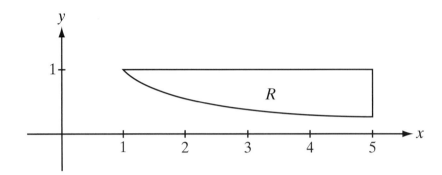

3. Let R be the region bounded by the graphs of $y = \dfrac{1}{x}$, the horizontal line $y = 1$, and the vertical line $x = 5$, as shown in the figure above.

    (a)   Find the area of R.

    (b)   Write, but do not evaluate, an integral expression that gives the volume of the solid generated when R is revolved about the horizontal line $y = 2$.

    (c)   The region R is the base of a solid. For each x, $1 \le x \le 5$, the cross section perpendicular to the x-axis has an area of $2^x - 2$. Find the volume of the solid.

    (a)   Find the area of R.

(b)   Write, but do not evaluate, an integral expression that gives the volume of the solid generated when R is revolved about the horizontal line $y = 2$.

(c)   The region R is the base of a solid. For each x, $1 \le x \le 5$, the cross section perpendicular to the x-axis has an area of $2^x - 2$. Find the volume of the solid.

4. A cylindrical tank is initially filled with water to a depth of 16 feet. A valve in the bottom is opened and the water runs out. The depth, h, of the water in the tank decreases at a rate proportional to the square root of the depth, that is, $\dfrac{dh}{dt} = -k\sqrt{h}$, h is measured in feet, k is a constant, $0 < k < 1$, and t is expressed in hours.

   (a)   Find the solution of the differential equation for h in terms of k and t.
   (b)   After the valve is opened, the water falls to a depth of 12.25 feet in 8 hours. Find the value of k.
   (c)   How many hours after the valve was first opened will the tank be completely empty?

   (a)   Find the solution of the differential equation for h in terms of k and t.

(b) After the valve is opened, the water falls to a depth of 12.25 feet in 8 hours. Find the value of k.

(c) How many hours after the valve was first opened will the tank be completely empty?

5. Consider the curve $y = 4x - x^3$ and chord AB joining points A $(-3, 15)$ and B $(3, -15)$ on the curve.

   (a)   Find the x- and y-coordinates of the point(s) on the curve where the tangent line is parallel to chord AB.

   (b)   Write an expression without absolute value for the vertical distance, V, between the curve and chord AB for $0 < x < 3$.

   (c)   Find the maximum vertical distance between the curve and chord AB for $0 < x < 3$.

   (a)   Find the x- and y-coordinates of the point(s) on the curve where the tangent line is parallel to chord AB.

(b) Write an expression without absolute value for the vertical distance, V, between the curve and chord AB for $0 < x < 3$.

(c) Find the maximum vertical distance between the curve and chord AB for $0 < x < 3$.

6. Let the derivative of a function f be $f'(x) = \ln(\sin x)$ and let $f\left(\frac{\pi}{2}\right) = 1$.

   (a) Write an equation of the line tangent to f at $x = \frac{\pi}{2}$.

   (b) Write an expression for $f''(x)$.

   (c) Does f change concavity at $x = \frac{\pi}{2}$? Justify your answer.

   (d) Find the Taylor polynomial of degree three centered at $x = \frac{\pi}{2}$, which approximates f.

   (a) Write an equation of the line tangent to f at $x = \frac{\pi}{2}$.

   (b) Write an expression for $f''(x)$.

(c)   Does f change concavity at $x = \frac{\pi}{2}$? Justify your answer.

(d)   Find the Taylor polynomial of degree three centered at $x = \frac{\pi}{2}$, which approximates f.

NO TESTING MATERIAL ON THIS PAGE

SAMPLE EXAMINATION V
SECTION I PART A

NO CALCULATOR IS ALLOWED IN THIS SECTION.

Directions: Solve each of the following problems, using the available space for scratch work. After examining the form of the choices, decide which is the best of the choices given. Do not spend too much time on any one problem.

In this exam:

(1) Unless otherwise specified, the domain of a function f is assumed to be the set of all real numbers x for which $f(x)$ is a real number.

(2) The inverse of a trigonometric function f may be indicated using the inverse function notation f^{-1} or with the prefix "arc" (e.g., $\sin^{-1} x = \arcsin x$)

1. If $y = (2x^2 + 1)^4$, then $\dfrac{dy}{dx} =$

   (A) $4(2x^2 + 1)^3$

   (B) $4x(2x^2 + 1)^3$

   (C) $16(2x^2 + 1)^3$

   (D) $16x(2x^2 + 1)^3$

$4(2x^2 + 1)^3 \cdot 4x$

Answer

 2. $\displaystyle \int x\sqrt{x^2 + 1}\,dx =$ U-SUB

$\dfrac{1}{2}x^2 \cdot \dfrac{2}{3}(x^2+1)^{3/2}$

   (A) $\dfrac{3}{4}(x^2 + 1)^{\frac{3}{2}} + C$

 (B) $\dfrac{1}{3}(x^2 + 1)^{\frac{3}{2}} + C$

$\approx \dfrac{1}{3}x^2(x^2+1)^{3/2} + C$

   (C) $\dfrac{2}{3}(x^2 + 1)^{\frac{3}{2}} + C$

   (D) $\dfrac{1}{3}x^2(x^2 + 1)^{\frac{3}{2}} + C$

Answer

3. The position of a particle moving in the xy-plane is given by the parametric equations $x(t) = \frac{1}{4}t^4 - t^3 - 2t^2$ and $y(t) = \frac{1}{4}t^4 - 8t^2$. The particle is at rest when $t =$

(A) 0 and 4 only

(B) -1, 0, and 4 only

(C) -4, 0, and 4 only

(D) $-4, -1, 0,$ and 4

$$t^2\left(\frac{1}{4}t^2 - t - 2\right)$$

$$0,$$

$$x'(t) = t^3 - 3t^2 - 4t = t(t^2 - 3t - 4) = t(t-4)(t+1) = 0, 4, -1$$

$$y'(t) = t^3 - 16t = t(t^2 - 16) = t(t-4)(t+4) = 0, 4, -4$$

Answer

4. A curve in the plane is defined parametrically by the equations $x = 2t + 3$ and $y = t^2 + 2t$. An equation of the line tangent to the curve at $t = 1$ is

$= 5 \qquad = 3$

$\partial x = 2 \qquad \partial y = 2t + 2$

$= 2 \qquad \partial y = 4$

$\frac{\partial y}{\partial x} = 2$

(A) $y = 2x - 7$

(B) $y = x - 2$

(C) $y = 2x$

(D) $y = 2x - 1$

$(5, 3)$

$y = 2x + b$

$3 = 10 + b$

$-7 = b$

Answer

5. $\int_0^8 \dfrac{1}{\sqrt[3]{8-x}}\, dx$ is

   (A) 2   (B) 6   (C) 12   (D) nonexistent

$$\int_0^8 \left((8-x)^{-1/3} \right)$$

$-\frac{1}{3}+1=\frac{2}{3}$

$$\frac{3}{2}(8-x)^{2/3} \Big|_0^8$$

$$\frac{3}{2}(0)^{2/3} - \frac{3}{2}(8)^{2/3}$$

$$\frac{3}{2}(8)^{2/3}$$

$$\frac{3}{2}(4) = 6$$

Answer

6. $\int x \sin x\, dx =$

   (A) $-\dfrac{1}{2}x^2 \cos x + C$

   (B) $x \cos x - \sin x + C$

   (C) $-x \cos x + \sin x + C$

   (D) $-x \cos x - \sin x + C$

$-\sin x (x) + \cos(x) - \sin x$

$-1(\cos x) + (-x)(\sin x) + \sin x$

Answer

7. Let f be a differentiable function for all x. Which of the following must be true?

$\quad$ I. $\dfrac{d}{dx}\displaystyle\int_0^3 f(x)\,dx = f(x)$

$\quad$ II. $\displaystyle\int_3^x f'(x)\,dx = f(x)$ $\times$

$\quad$ III. $\dfrac{d}{dx}\displaystyle\int_3^x f(x)\,dx = f(x)$

(A) II only

(B) III only

(C) I and II only

(D) II and III only

Answer

---

8. If $\sin(xy) = x^2$, then $\dfrac{dy}{dx} =$

(A) $2x\sec(xy)$

(B) $2x\sec(xy) - y$

(C) $\dfrac{2x\sec(xy)}{y}$

(D) $\dfrac{2x\sec(xy) - y}{x}$

$\cos(xy)\cdot\left(y + x\dfrac{dy}{dx}\right) = 2x$

$\cos(xy)\left(y + x\dfrac{dy}{dx}\right) = 2x$

$\left(y + x\dfrac{dy}{dx}\right) = 2x\sec(xy)$

Answer

9. For all x in the closed interval $[1,4]$, the function g is concave upwards. Which of the following tables could be the values of $g(x)$?

(A)

x	$g(x)$
1	-10
2	-7
3	-6
4	-2

3
1
4

(B)

x	$g(x)$
1	4
2	6
3	9
4	14

2
3
5

(C)

x	$g(x)$
1	0
2	5
3	7
4	12

5
2
5

(D)

x	$g(x)$
1	-2
2	-1
3	5
4	3

Answer

10. $\displaystyle\int \frac{dx}{x^2 + 4x} =$

(A) $\displaystyle\int \frac{dx}{x^2} + \int \frac{dx}{4x}$

(B) $\displaystyle\int \frac{dx}{x} - \int \frac{dx}{x+4}$

(C) $\displaystyle\int \frac{dx}{4x} + \int \frac{dx}{4(x+4)}$

(D) $\displaystyle\int \frac{dx}{4x} - \int \frac{dx}{4(x+4)}$

$1 = \int \frac{a}{x} + \frac{b}{x+4}$

$1 = b(x) + a(x+4)$

$x = 0$

$1 = \frac{?}{} 4a$

$a = \frac{1}{4}$

$x = -4$

$1 = -4b$

$-\frac{1}{4} = b$

$\int \frac{\frac{1}{4}}{x} \quad -\int \frac{\frac{1}{4}}{x+4}$

Answer

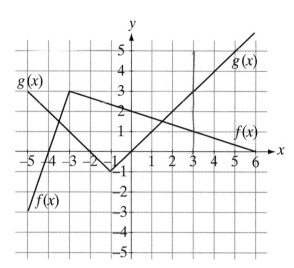

Handwritten notes (right side):
$f'(x)g(x) + g'(x)f(x)$
$f'(3)3 + g'(3)$
$f'(3)3 + 1$
$\frac{2-1}{0-3} = -\frac{1}{3}$ $-1+1$

11. The functions f and g are piecewise linear functions whose graphs are shown above. If $h(x) = f(x)\,g(x)$, then $h'(3) =$

(A) 0   (B) $\frac{2}{3}$ (C) $-\frac{1}{3}$ (D) -8

Answer

12. The Taylor Series of a function $f(x)$ about $x = 3$ is given by

$$f(x) = 1 + \frac{3(x-3)}{1!} + \frac{5(x-3)^2}{2!} + \frac{7(x-3)^3}{3!} + \cdots + \frac{(2n+1)(x-3)^n}{n!} + \cdots$$

What is the value of $f'''(3)$, the third derivative of f at $x = 3$?

 (A) $\frac{7}{6}$ (B) $\frac{5}{2}$ (C) 5   (D) 7

Answer

13. The position vector of a particle moving in the xy-plane is given by $\left\langle e^{-2t}, \dfrac{1}{t+1} \right\rangle$. Which of the following expressions represents the speed of the particle at $t = 2$?

(A) $\left\langle \left| \dfrac{-2}{e^4} \right|, \left| \dfrac{-1}{9} \right| \right\rangle$

(B) $\sqrt{1 + \left(\dfrac{-1/9}{-2/e^4} \right)^2}$

(C) $\sqrt{\left(\dfrac{-2}{e^4} \right)^2 + \left(\dfrac{-1}{9} \right)^2}$

(D) $\displaystyle\int_0^2 \sqrt{\left(\dfrac{-2}{e^{2t}} \right)^2 + \left(\dfrac{-1}{(t+1)^2} \right)^2} \, dt$

Answer

14. The slope field for the differential equation $\dfrac{dy}{dx} = \dfrac{x^2 y + y^2 x}{3x + y}$ will have horizontal segments when

(A) $x = 0$ or $y = 0$, only

(B) $y = -x$ only

(C) $xy = 0$ only

(D) $x = 0$, or $y = 0$, or $y = -x$

Answer

x	1	3	7	8	10
$f(x)$	-2	0	3	3	-4

15. The function f is continuous on the closed interval $[1,10]$ and has the values shown in the table above. Using the intervals $[1,3], [3,7], [7,8]$ and $[8,10]$, what is the approximation of $\int_1^{10} f(x)\, dx$ obtained from a right Riemann sum?

(A) 5   (B) 6   (C) 7   (D) 13

Answer

16. What are the first four nonzero terms in the power series expansion of e^{-4x} about $x = 0$?

(A) $1 - 4x + 8x^2 - 32x^3$

(B) $1 - 4x - 2x^2 - \dfrac{2}{3}x^3$

(C) $1 - 4x + 8x^2 - \dfrac{32}{3}x^3$

(D) $1 - 4x + 8x^2 - \dfrac{64}{3}x^3$

Answer

17. On the open interval $a < x < b$ the graph of g', the derivative of g, is continuous and differentiable. On this interval the graph of g' has several local maximums, several local minimums and several zeros. The graph of g changes from concave down to concave up at which points on the graph of g'?

(A) At the zeros where g' changes from positive to negative

(B) At the zeros where g' changes from negative to positive

(C) At the local maximums of g'

(D) At the local minimums of g'

Answer

18. $\int_{e}^{e^2} \dfrac{dx}{x \ln x} =$

(A) $\ln 2$ (B) $\dfrac{1}{2}$ (C) 1 (D) 2

Answer

19. Let $f(x)$ be a differentiable function on the interval $0 \le x \le 1$, and let $g(x) = f(3x)$. The table below gives values of $f'(x)$, the derivative of $f(x)$. What is the value of $g'(0.1)$?

x	0.1	0.2	0.3	0.4	0.5	0.6
$f'(x)$	1.01	1.041	1.096	1.179	1.298	1.486

(A) 1.096   (B) 1.486   (C) 3.030   (D) 3.288

Answer

20. Which of the following integrals gives the total area of the region shared by both polar curves $r = 2 \cos \theta$ and $r = 2 \sin \theta$?

(A) $2 \int_0^{\frac{\pi}{4}} \sin^2 \theta \, d\theta$

(B) $4 \int_0^{\frac{\pi}{4}} \sin^2 \theta \, d\theta$

(C) $2 \int_0^{\frac{\pi}{2}} \sin^2 \theta \, d\theta$

(D) $4 \int_0^{\frac{\pi}{4}} \cos^2 \theta \, d\theta$

Answer

21. $\lim\limits_{h \to 0} \dfrac{2(x+h)^5 - 5(x+h)^3 - 2x^5 + 5x^3}{h}$ is

(A) $10x^3 - 15x$

(B) $10x^4 + 15x^2$

(C) $10x^4 - 15x^2$

(D) $-10x^4 + 15x^2$

Answer

22. If $\displaystyle\int_2^8 f(x)\, dx = -10$ and $\displaystyle\int_2^4 f(x)\, dx = 6$, then $\displaystyle\int_8^4 f(x)\, dx =$

(A) -16 (B) -4 (C) 4 (D) 16

Answer

23. If the graph of $y = x^3 + ax^2 + bx - 8$ has a point of inflection at $(2,0)$, what is the value of b?

(A) 4

(B) 8

(C) 12

(D) The value of b cannot be determined from the given information.

Answer

24. The position of a particle in the xy-plane is given by $x = 4t^2$ and $y = \sqrt{t}$.
    At $t = 4$, the acceleration vector is

(A) $\left\langle 8, -\dfrac{1}{64} \right\rangle$

(B) $\left\langle 8, -\dfrac{1}{32} \right\rangle$

(C) $\left\langle 8, \dfrac{1}{32} \right\rangle$

(D) $\left\langle 8, \dfrac{1}{4} \right\rangle$

Answer

25. If n is a positive integer, then $\lim\limits_{n \to \infty} \dfrac{1}{n}\left[\left(\dfrac{1}{n}\right)^2 + \left(\dfrac{2}{n}\right)^2 + \cdots + \left(\dfrac{n-1}{n}\right)^2\right]$ can be expressed as

(A) $\displaystyle\int_0^1 \dfrac{1}{x^2}\,dx$

(B) $\displaystyle\int_0^1 x^2\,dx$

(C) $\displaystyle\int_0^1 \dfrac{2}{x^2}\,dx$

(D) $\displaystyle\int_0^2 x^2\,dx$

Answer

26. What are all the values of x for which the series $x - \dfrac{x^2}{2} + \dfrac{x^3}{3} - \dfrac{x^4}{4} + \cdots + (-1)^{n+1}\dfrac{x^n}{n} + \cdots$ converges?

(A) $-1 \le x \le 1$

(B) $-1 \le x < 1$

(C) $-1 < x \le 1$

(D) $-1 < x < 1$

Answer

27. $\displaystyle\sum_{n-0}^{\infty} \frac{(-1)^n (\pi)^{2n}}{(2n)!} =$

(A) -1 (B) 1 (C) π (D) $\dfrac{\pi}{2}$

Answer

28. If $\dfrac{dy}{dx} = \dfrac{x}{y}$ and $y(3) = 4$, then

(A) $y^2 - x^2 = 7$

(B) $x^2 - y^2 = 5^2$

(C) $x^2 - y^2 = 7$

(D) $y^2 - x^2 = 5$

Answer

29. The Maclaurin series for a function f is given by $\sum_{n=1}^{\infty} \dfrac{x^n}{2n}$. What is the value of $f^{(4)}(0)$, the fourth derivative of f at $x = 0$?

(A) 2   (B) 3   (C) 4   (D) 5

Answer

x	1	2	3	4	5	6	7
$f'(x)$	5	0	-3	0	-2	0	4

30. Let $g(x) = \displaystyle\int_{1}^{x} f(t)\, dt$. The table above gives selected values of f', the derivative of f, on the interval $1 \le x \le 7$. If f' is continuous and has only the three zeros as shown in the table, for which values of x does g have a point of inflection?

(A) 2 only

(B) 6 only

(C) 2 and 6 only

(D) 2, 4, and 6

Answer

SECTION I PART B

A GRAPHING CALCULATOR IS REQUIRED FOR SOME QUESTIONS IN THIS SECTION.

Directions: Solve each of the following problems, using available space for scratch work. After examining the form of the choices, decide which is the best of the choices given. Do not spend too much time on any one problem.

In this exam:

(1) The exact numerical value of the correct answer does not always appear among the choices given. When this happens, select from among the choices the number that best approximates the exact numerical value.

(2) Unless otherwise specified, the domain of a function f is assumed to be the set of all real numbers x for which $f(x)$ is a real number.

(3) The inverse of a trigonometric function f may be indicated using the inverse function notation f^{-1} or with the prefix "arc" (e.g., $\sin^{-1}x = \arcsin x$)

31. Suppose that $f(x)$, $f'(x)$, and $f''(x)$ are continuous for all real numbers x, and that f has the following properties.

      I. f is negative on $(-\infty, 6)$ and positive on $(6, \infty)$.

     II. f is increasing on $(-\infty, 8)$ and decreasing on $(8, \infty)$.

    III. f is concave down on $(-\infty, 10)$ and concave up on $(10, \infty)$.

Of the following, which has the <u>least</u> numerical value?

(A) $f'(0)$ (B) $f''(4)$ (C) $f''(10)$ (D) $f''(12)$

Answer

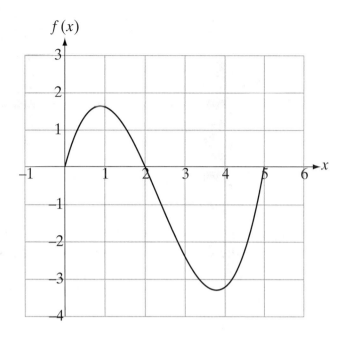

32. The figure above shows the graph of a function $f(x)$ on the interval $[0,5]$. Which of the following definite integrals has the greatest value?

(A) $\int_0^2 f(x)\, dx$

(B) $\int_0^3 f(x)\, dx$

(C) $\int_0^4 f(x)\, dx$

(D) $\int_0^5 f(x)\, dx$

Answer

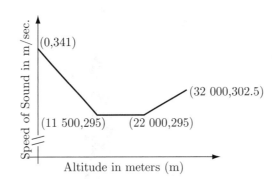

33. In the earth's atmosphere the speed of sound is a function of the altitude. The figure above consisting of 3 line segments, shows the speed of sound $s(a)$ in m/sec. as a function of altitude, a in meters. The graph is not drawn to scale. What is the average speed of sound in m/sec. on the interval $[0, 32000]$?

(A) 295   (B) 303.9   (C) 304.4   (D) 306.8

Answer

34. If $f'(x) = (x-a)(x-b)(x-c)$ and $a < b < c$, then which of the following could be the graph of $f(x)$?

(A)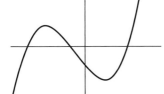

(B)

(C)

(D)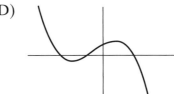

Answer

35. The density of a thin metal rod one meter long at a distance of x meters from one end is given by $\rho(x) = 1 + (1 - x)^2$ grams per meter. What is the mass, in grams, of this rod?

(A) 1.333   (B) 1.500   (C) 1.667   (D) 2

Answer

36. If $\displaystyle\sum_{n=1}^{\infty} |a_n|$ converges, then which of the following is true?

I. $\displaystyle\sum_{n=1}^{\infty} a_n$ converges.

II. $\displaystyle\sum_{n=1}^{\infty} a_n$ is absolutely convergent.

III. $\displaystyle\sum_{n=1}^{\infty} -a_n$ converges.

(A) I only

(B) II only

(C) III only

(D) I, II, and III

Answer

37. The base of a solid is the region enclosed by the graph of $y = 3(x-2)^2$ and the coordinate axes. If every cross section perpendicular to the x-axis is a square, then the volume of the solid is

(A) 19.2   (B) 24.0   (C) 25.6   (D) 57.6

Answer

38. Let f be a function whose seventh derivative is $f^{(7)}(x) = 10{,}000 \cos x$ where $x = 1$ is in the interval of convergence of the power series for this function. Using the Lagrange error bound the Taylor polynomial of degree six centered at $x = 0$ will approximate $f(1)$ with an error of not more than

(A) 1.98×10^{-4} (B) 3.21×10^{-2} (C) 1.072   (D) 1.984

Answer

39. If f is an antiderivative of $\dfrac{\tan^2 x}{x^2 + 1}$ such that $f(1) = \dfrac{1}{2}$, then $f(0) =$

(A) 0.155   (B) 0.345   (C) 0.845   (D) 1

Answer

40. The current price of a compact car is \$14,500. The price of a compact car is changing at a rate of $120 + 180\sqrt{t}$ dollars per year. What will be the approximate price of a compact car five years from now?

(A) \$15,020   (B) \$15,300   (C) \$16,440   (D) \$18,120

Answer

41. If $0 \leq k \leq \frac{\pi}{2}$ and the area of the region in the first quadrant under the graph of $y = 2x - \sin x$ from 0 to k is 0.1, then $k =$

   (A) 0.444   (B) 0.623   (C) 0.883   (D) 1.062

Answer

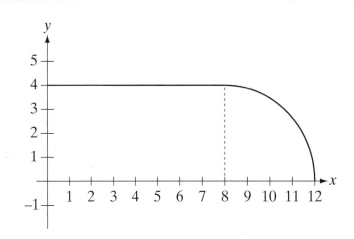

42. As shown in the figure above, the function $f(x)$ consists of a line segment from $(0, 4)$ to $(8, 4)$ and one-quarter of a circle with a radius of 4. What is the average (mean) value of this function on the interval $[0, 12]$?

   (A) 3.714   (B) 6.855   (C) 22.283   (D) 44.566

Answer

43. The mass, $m(t)$, in grams, of a tumor t weeks after it begins growing is given by $m(t) = \dfrac{te^t}{800}$. What is the average rate of change, in grams per week, during the fifth week of growth?

(A) 0.341   (B) 0.619   (C) 0.655   (D) 1.113

Answer

44. If $g(x) = e^{2x}$, then $\displaystyle\lim_{h \to 0} \frac{g(1+h) - g(1-h)}{h}$ is

(A) e^2 (B) $2e^2$ (C) $4e^2$ (D) nonexistent

Answer

45. The closed interval $[0,\pi]$ is partitioned into n equal subdivisions each of length $\Delta x = \frac{\pi}{n}$ by the numbers $x_0, x_1, x_2 \ldots, x_{n-1}, x_n$, with $0 = x_0 < x_1 < x_2 < \ldots < x_{n-1} < x_n = \pi$.

The $\displaystyle\lim_{n \to \infty} \sum_{i=1}^{n} x_i \cos(x_i) \Delta x$ is

(A) -2 (B) -1 (C) 1 (D) 2

Answer

FREE-RESPONSE QUESTIONS — GENERAL INSTRUCTIONS

For each part of Section II, you may wish to look over the problems before starting to work on them. It is not expected that everyone will be able to complete all parts of all problems. All problems are given equal weight, but the parts of a particular problem are not necessarily given equal weight.

YOU SHOULD WRITE ALL WORK FOR EACH PART OF EACH PROBLEM IN THE SPACE PROVIDED FOR THAT PART. Be sure to write clearly and legibly. If you make an error, you may save time by crossing it out rather than trying to erase it. Erased or crossed-out work will not be graded. Manage your time carefully.

- Show all your work, even though a question may not explicitly remind you to do so. Clearly label any functions, graphs, tables, or other objects that you use. Your work will be graded on the correctness and completeness of your methods as well as your answers. Answers without supporting work will usually not receive credit.

- Justifications require that you give mathematical (noncalculator) reasons.

- Your work must be expressed in standard mathematical notation rather than calculator syntax. For example, $\int_1^5 x^2\,dx$ may not be written as fnInt(X^2, X, 1, 5).

- Unless otherwise specified, answers (numeric or algebraic) need not be simplified.

- If you use decimal approximations in calculations, your work will be graded on accuracy. Unless otherwise specified, your final answers should be accurate to three places after the decimal point.

- Unless otherwise specified, the domain of a function f is assumed to be the set of all real numbers x for which $f(x)$ is a real number.

SECTION II PART A: 30 Minutes, Questions 1,2

A graphing calculator is required.

During the timed portion for Part A, you may work only on the problems in Part A. Write your solution to each part of each problem in the space provided.

On Part A, you are permitted to use your calculator to solve an equation, find the derivative of a function at a point, or calculate the value of a definite integral. However, you must clearly indicate the setup of your programs, you must show the mathematical steps necessary to produce your results.

Do not go on to Part B until you are told to do so.

SECTION II PART B: 60 Minutes, Questions 3,4,5,6

Write your solution to each part of each problem in the space provided for that part. During the timed portion for Part B, you may continue to work on the problems in Part A without the use of any calculator.

1. An object moving along a curve in the xy-plane is at position $(x(t), y(t))$ at time t with $x(t) = 2 + \sqrt{t}$ and $\dfrac{dy}{dt} = te^t - e^t$ for $t \geq 0$.

   (a) Find the speed of the object at time $t = 3$.
   (b) Find the total distance traveled by the object over the time interval $0 \leq t \leq 3$.
   (c) At what time t is the object at the point on the curve where the line tangent to the curve has slope 5?
   (d) At time $t = 0$, the object is at position $(2, -2)$. Find $y(3)$.

   (a) Find the speed of the object at time $t = 3$.

   (b) Find the total distance traveled by the object over the time interval $0 \leq t \leq 3$.

(c)   At what time t is the object at the point on the curve where the line tangent to the curve has slope 5?

(d)   At time $t = 0$, the object is at position $(2, -2)$. Find $y(3)$.

2. Two walkers start at the same time from the same place and travel in the same direction with velocities given by $A(t) = 1 - e^{-t}$ miles per minute and $B(t) = 0.2(e^t - 1)$ miles per minute and $t > 0$. They travel until they have the same velocity.

(a) On the axes provided, sketch the graphs of the velocities and label each.
(b) When they have the same velocity, which person has traveled farther? Use the graph to explain your reasoning.
(c) Write an expression which represents the distance between the walkers at any time $t > 0$.
(d) At what time is the distance between them the greatest? Explain your reasoning.

(a) On the axes provided, sketch the graphs of the velocities and label each.

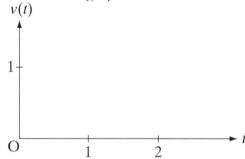

(b) When they have the same velocity, which person has traveled farther? Use the graph to explain your reasoning.

(c)   Write an expression which represents the distance between the walkers at any time $t > 0$.

(d)   At what time is the distance between them the greatest? Explain your reasoning.

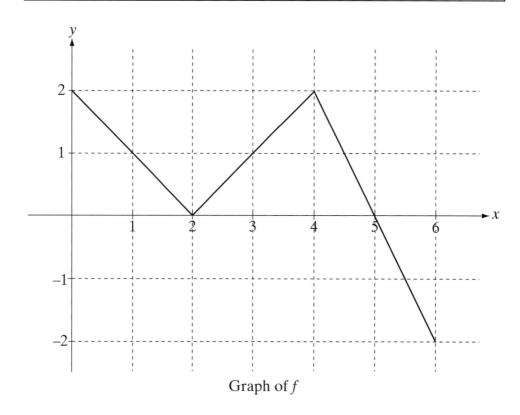

Graph of f

3. The function f is defined and continuous on the closed interval $[0,6]$. The graph of $y = f(x)$ consists

of three line segments as shown above. Let $g(x) = -x + \int_{2}^{x} f(t)\, dt$.

(a)   Find $g(3)$ and $g'(3)$.
(b)   Find the x-coordinate of the 3 critical points of g on the open interval $(0,6)$. Show the computation that leads to your answer.
(c)   Find $g''(x)$ in terms of f.
(d)   For each critical point found in part (b), state whether it is a relative maximum, a relative minimum or neither. Justify your answers.

(a)   Find $g(3)$ and $g'(3)$.

(b) Find the x-coordinate of the 3 critical points of g on the open interval (0,6). Show the computation that leads to your answer.

(c) Find $g''(x)$ in terms of f.

(d) For each critical point found in part (b), state whether it is a relative maximum, a relative minimum or neither. Justify your answers.

hours	0	0.1	0.2	0.3	0.4	0.5	0.6	0.7	0.8	0.9	1.0
a m/h/h	0	90	90	80	78	80	60	40	30	10	0

4. A train, initially stopped, begins moving. The table above shows the train's acceleration *a*, in miles/hour/hour as a function of time measured in hours.

Let $f(t) = \int_0^t a(x)\, dx$.

(a) Use the midpoint Riemann sum with 5 subdivisions of equal length to approximate $f(1)$.
(b) Explain what $f(1)$ is, and give its units of measure.
(c) Assume that the acceleration is constant on the interval $[0.1, 0.2]$. How far does the train travel during this interval? Include units of measure. Show how you arrived at your answer.

(a) Use the midpoint Riemann sum with 5 subdivisions of equal length to approximate $f(1)$.

(b)   Explain what $f(1)$ is, and give its units of measure.

(c)   Assume that the acceleration is constant on the interval $[0.1, 0.2]$. How far does the train travel during this interval? Include units of measure. Show how you arrived at your answer.

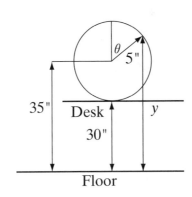

35"   Desk   y

30"

Floor

5. As shown in the figure above, a clock sits on a desk so that its center is 35 inches from the floor. The *minute hand* is 5 inches long. Let θ be the angle between the 12 o'clock position and the minute's hand position at any time t minutes after the hour. (Note: θ is measured clockwise and in radians).

(a) Using a trigonometric function of θ, write an expression for y, the distance from the tip of the minute hand to the floor.

(b) Express θ as a function of t.

(c) In terms of θ, find an expression for $\dfrac{dy}{dt}$, the rate at which y changes.

(d) At how many minutes after the hour is y increasing most rapidly? Use $\dfrac{dy}{dt}$ to justify your answer.

(a) Using a trigonometric function of θ, write an expression for y, the distance from the tip of the minute hand to the floor.

(b)   Express θ as a function of t.

(c)   In terms of θ, find an expression for $\dfrac{dy}{dt}$, the rate at which y changes.

(d)   At how many minutes after the hour is y increasing most rapidly? Use $\dfrac{dy}{dt}$ to justify your answer.

6. The differential equation $14 = \dfrac{dT}{dt} + 0.01T$ models the temperature, T, above room temperature, of an electric burner. T is measured in degrees Fahrenheit (F°) and $t \geq 0$ is in seconds.

(a) Find the general solution of the differential equation in terms of a constant k.

(b) When the burner is first turned on at room temperature, $T = 0°F$. Use this fact to find the value of the constant k.

(c) The Safety Standards Board has determined that this type of burner is unsafe if its temperature can exceed 1500°F. Is this burner safe or unsafe? Justify your answer.

(a) Find the general solution of the differential equation in terms of a constant k.

(b)   When the burner is first turned on at room temperature, $T = 0°F$. Use this fact to find the value of the constant k.

(c)   The Safety Standards Board has determined that this type of burner is unsafe if its temperature can exceed 1500°F. Is this burner safe or unsafe? Justify your answer.

SAMPLE EXAMINATION VI
SECTION I PART A

NO CALCULATOR IS ALLOWED IN THIS SECTION.

Directions: Solve each of the following problems, using the available space for scratch work. After examining the form of the choices, decide which is the best of the choices given. Do not spend too much time on any one problem.

In this exam:

(1) Unless otherwise specified, the domain of a function f is assumed to be the set of all real numbers x for which $f(x)$ is a real number.

(2) The inverse of a trigonometric function f may be indicated using the inverse function notation f^{-1} or with the prefix "arc" (e.g., $\sin^{-1} x = \arcsin x$)

1. Suppose that $f(x)$ is a twice-differentiable function on the closed interval $[a,b]$. If there is a number c, $a < c < b$, for which $f'(c) = 0$, which of the following must be true?

      I. $f(a) = f(b)$

      II. f has a relative extremum at $x = c$.

      III. f has a point of inflection at $x = c$.

(A) None

(B) II only

(C) I and II

(D) II and III

Answer

2. $\int_0^2 xe^x \, dx =$

(A) $e^2 - 1$ (B) $e^2 + 1$ (C) $e^4 - e^2 + 1$ (D) $e^4 + e^2 - 1$

Answer

3. A particle moves in the xy-plane so that at any time t its coordinates are $x = \alpha \cos \beta t$ and $y = \alpha \sin \beta t$, where α and β are constants. The y-component of the acceleration vector of the particle at any time t is

(A) $-\beta^2 y$

(B) $-\beta^2 x$

(C) $-\alpha\beta \sin \beta t$

(D) $-\alpha\beta \cos \beta t$

Answer

4. An equation of the line tangent to the curve $y = \dfrac{3x + 4}{4x - 3}$ at the point $(1,7)$ is

(A) $y + 25x = 32$

(B) $y - 31x = -24$

(C) $y + 5x = 12$

(D) $y - 25x = -18$

Answer

5. The power series for $\dfrac{1}{x+1}$ is $\displaystyle\sum_{n=0}^{\infty}(-1)^n x^n$. Which of the following is a power series expansion of $\dfrac{x^2}{1+x^4}$?

(A) $x^2 + x^6 + x^{10} + x^{14} + \cdots$

(B) $x^6 - x^{10} + x^{14} - x^{18} + \cdots$

(C) $1 - x^6 + x^{10} - x^{14} + \cdots$

(D) $x^2 - x^6 + x^{10} - x^{14} + \cdots$

Answer

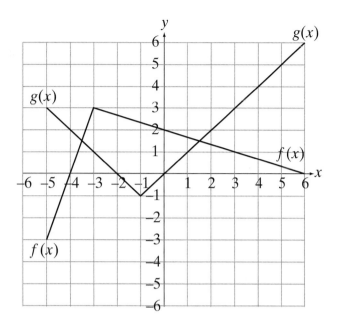

6. The functions f and g are piecewise linear functions whose graphs are shown above. If $h(x) = f(g(x))$, then $h'(-3) =$

(A) -3 (B) $-\dfrac{1}{3}$ (C) $\dfrac{1}{3}$ (D) 3

Answer

7. What is the value of $\sum_{n=1}^{\infty} \dfrac{3^{n+1}}{4^n}$?

(A) 3   (B) 9   (C) 12   (D) The series diverges.

Answer

8. $\displaystyle\int_0^3 \dfrac{x}{\sqrt{x^2+16}}\,dx =$

(A) 1   (B) 2   (C) 3   (D) 4

Answer

9. If $y = \ln(3x + 5)$, then $\dfrac{d^2y}{dx^2} =$

(A) $\dfrac{3}{(3x+5)^2}$

(B) $\dfrac{9}{(3x+5)^2}$

(C) $\dfrac{-9}{(3x+5)^2}$

(D) $\dfrac{-3}{(3x+5)^2}$

Answer

10. $\displaystyle\int_{-1}^{1} \dfrac{dx}{x^2 + 5x + 6} =$

(A) $\ln\dfrac{3}{2}$ (B) $\ln\dfrac{1}{4}$ (C) $\ln\dfrac{2}{3}$ (D) $\ln 6$

Answer

11. A function $f(x)$ has a vertical asymptote at $x = 2$. The derivative of $f(x)$ is positive for all $x \neq 2$. Which of the following statements are true?

$$\text{I.} \quad \lim_{x \to 2} f(x) = +\infty$$

$$\text{II.} \quad \lim_{x \to 2^-} f(x) = +\infty$$

$$\text{III.} \quad \lim_{x \to 2^+} f(x) = +\infty$$

(A) I only

(B) II only

(C) III only

(D) I, II, and III

Answer

12. If $x = 2t^2$ and $y = t^3$, then $\dfrac{d^2 y}{dx^2}$ at $t = 3$ is

(A) $\dfrac{1}{16}$ (B) $\dfrac{3}{4}$ (C) $\dfrac{1}{4}$ (D) $\dfrac{9}{4}$

Answer

13. The Taylor series for a function f about $x = 0$ converges for $-1 \leq x \leq 1$. The nth-degree Taylor polynomial for f about $x = 0$ is given by $P_n(x) = \sum_{k=1}^{n} (-1)^k \dfrac{x^k}{(k+2)(k+3)}$. Which of the following is the least value of M for which the alternating series error bound guarantees that $|f(1) - P_3(1)| \leq M$?

(A) $\dfrac{1}{4!\,(42)}$ (B) $\dfrac{1}{3!\,(30)}$ (C) $\dfrac{1}{30}$ (D) $\dfrac{1}{42}$

Answer

14. $\displaystyle\int_{-\infty}^{\infty} e^{-|x|}\, dx$ is

(A) 0   (B) 1   (C) 2   (D) divergent

Answer

15. What are all values of x for which the graph of $y = 6x^2 + \dfrac{x}{2} + 3 + \dfrac{6}{x}$ is concave downward?

(A) $x < -1$

(B) $-1 < x < 0$

(C) $x > -1$

(D) No values of x

Answer

16. What is the area of the largest rectangle with lower base on the x-axis and upper vertices on the curve $y = 12 - x^2$?

(A) 12   (B) 16   (C) 32   (D) 48

Answer

17. The efficiency of an automobile engine is given by the continuous function $r(c)$ where r is measured in liters/kilometer and c is measured in kilometers. What are the units of $\int_0^5 r(c)\, dc$?

(A) liters

(B) kilometers

(C) liters/kilometer

(D) kilometers/liter

Answer

18. $f(x) = x^3 + 2x^2 - 1$ and $f(-1) = 0$. If $g(x) = f^{-1}(x)$, the value of $g'(0)$ is

(A) −1 (B) 0 (C) 1 (D) undefined

Answer

19. At what point on the curve $x^2 - y^2 + x = 2$ is the tangent line vertical?

(A) $(1,0)$ only

(B) $(-2,0)$ only

(C) $(1,0)$ and $(-2,0)$

(D) There is no vertical tangent line.

Answer

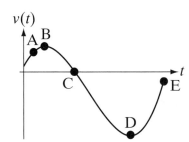

20. The figure above shows the graph of the velocity of an object moving on the x-axis as a function of time. Which of the marked points corresponds to the time when the object is farthest to the right?

(A) B   (B) C   (C) D   (D) E

Answer

21. If $\lim\limits_{x \to 2} \dfrac{f(x)}{x-2} = f'(2) = 0$, which of the following must be true?

    I. $f(2) = 0$.

    II. $f(x)$ is continuous at $x = 2$.

    III. $f(x)$ has a horizontal tangent line at $x = 2$.

(A) I and II only

(B) I and III only

(C) II and III only

(D) I, II, and III

Answer

22. Let $R(t)$ represent the rate at which water is leaking out of a tank, where t is measured in hours. Which of the following expressions represents the total amount of water in gallons that leaks out in the first three hours?

(A) $\displaystyle \int_0^3 R'(t)\, dt$

(B) $\displaystyle \int_0^3 R(t)\, dt$

(C) $\dfrac{1}{3}\displaystyle \int_0^3 R'(t)\, dt$

(D) $\dfrac{1}{3}\displaystyle \int_0^3 R(t)\, dt$

Answer

23. The derivative of $4x^2 \cos(x)$ is

(A) $8x \cos(x) + 4x^2 \sin(x)$

(B) $8x \cos(x) - 4x^2 \sin(x)$

(C) $-8x \cos(x) - 4x^2 \sin(x)$

(D) $-8x \cos(x) + 4x^2 \sin(x)$

Answer

24. If $\dfrac{dy}{dx} = y \cos x$ and $y = 3$ when $x = 0$, then $y =$

(A) $e^{\sin x} + 2$
(B) $e^{\sin x} + 3$
(C) $\sin x + 3e^x$
(D) $3e^{\sin x}$

Answer

25. On the interval $a \le x \le b$, the function f is positive, decreasing, and concave upwards. Which of the following has the greatest value?

(A) Left Riemann sum approximation of $\int_a^b f(x)\,dx$ with n subdivisions of equal length

(B) Right Riemann sum approximation of $\int_a^b f(x)\,dx$ with n subdivisions of equal length

(C) Midpoint Riemann sum approximation of $\int_a^b f(x)\,dx$ with n subdivisions of equal length

(D) Trapezoidal sum approximation of $\int_a^b f(x)\,dx$ with n subdivisions of equal length

Answer

26. Which of the following series converge?

I. $\displaystyle\sum_{n=1}^{\infty} \frac{4n+2}{(n+1)^2}$

II. $\displaystyle\sum_{n=1}^{\infty} \frac{1}{3^n - 2}$

III. $\displaystyle\sum_{n=1}^{\infty} \frac{2n+3}{n^3 - 4n}$

(A) II only   (B) III only   (C) II and III only   (D) I, II, and III

Answer

27. What are all values of x for which the series $\displaystyle\sum_{n=2}^{\infty} \frac{(-1)^n}{\ln n} x^n$ converges?

(A) $-1 < x < 1$

(B) $-1 \le x \le 1$

(C) $-1 \le x < 1$

(D) $-1 < x \le 1$

Answer

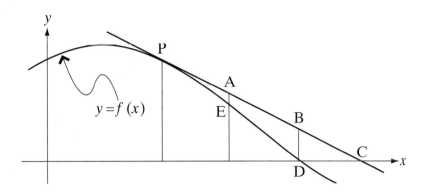

28. In the figure above $\overleftrightarrow{PC}$ is tangent to the graph of $y = f(x)$ at point P. Points A and B are on $\overleftrightarrow{PC}$ and points D and E are on the graph of $y = f(x)$. Which of the following statements are true?

    I. Euler's method uses the y-coordinate of point A to approximate the y-coordinate at point E.

    II. Euler's method uses the x-coordinate of point B to approximate the zero of the function $f(x)$ at point D.

    III. Euler's method uses the x-coordinate of point C to approximate a zero of the function $f(x)$ at point D.

(A) I only

(B) II only

(C) I and II only

(D) I and III only

Answer

29. Let f be a continuous function such that $\int_2^3 f(2x)\, dx = 8$. What is the value of $\int_4^6 f(x)\, dx$?

    (A) 8   (B) 12   (C) 16   (D) 32

Answer

30. What are all values of p for which $\int_1^\infty \frac{1}{x^{\pi p}}\, dx$ converges?

    (A) $p > 0$

    (B) $p > \dfrac{1}{\pi}$

    (C) $p > 1$

    (D) $p > \pi$

Answer

SECTION I PART B

A GRAPHING CALCULATOR IS REQUIRED FOR SOME QUESTIONS IN THIS SECTION.

Directions: Solve each of the following problems, using available space for scratch work. After examining the form of the choices, decide which is the best of the choices given. Do not spend too much time on any one problem.

In this exam:

(1) The exact numerical value of the correct answer does not always appear among the choices given. When this happens, select from among the choices the number that best approximates the exact numerical value.

(2) Unless otherwise specified, the domain of a function f is assumed to be the set of all real numbers x for which $f(x)$ is a real number.

(3) The inverse of a trigonometric function f may be indicated using the inverse function notation f^{-1} or with the prefix "arc" (e.g., $\sin^{-1}x = \arcsin x$)

Questions 31 and 32 refer to the following information.

The roof and walls of a storage building are built in the shape modeled by the curve $y(x) = 20 - \dfrac{x^6}{3{,}200{,}000}$. Each cross section cut perpendicular to the x-axis is a rectangle with a base of 50 feet and a height of y feet.

31. In cubic feet the volume of the building is approximately

   (A) 2,000   (B) 17,100   (C) 34,300   (D) 50,000

Answer
☐

32. What is the average height in feet of the storage building described above?

   (A) 8.571   (B) 11.920   (C) 15.071   (D) 17.143

Answer
☐

33. If $f(3) = 7$ and $f'(x) = \dfrac{\sin(1 + x^2)}{x^3 - 2x}$, then $f(5)$ is approximately

(A) -9.006 (B) -0.008 (C) 6.992 (D) 7.008

Answer

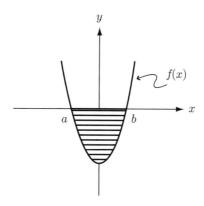

34. If f is the continuous function shown in the figure above, then the area of the shaded region is

(A) $\displaystyle\int_a^b f(x)\, dx$ (B) $\displaystyle\int_b^a f(x)\, dx$ (C) $\displaystyle\int_b^{-a} f(x)\, dx$ (D) $\displaystyle\int_{-a}^b f(x)\, dx$

Answer

35. A missile rises vertically from a point on the ground 75,000 feet from a radar station. If the missile is rising at the rate of 16,500 feet per minute at the instant when it is 38,000 feet high, what is the rate of change, in radians per minute, of the missile's angle of elevation from the radar station at this instant?

(A) 0.175   (B) 0.219   (C) 0.227   (D) 0.469

Answer

36. Let $f(x)$ be a function whose Taylor series converges for all x. If $\left| f^{(n)}(x) \right| < 1$ where $f^{(n)}(x)$ is the nth derivative of $f(x)$, what is the minimum number of terms of the Taylor series centered at $x = 1$ necessary to approximate $f(1.2)$ with a Lagrange error less than 0.00001 ?

(A) Three   (B) Four   (C) Five   (D) Six

Answer

37. The area enclosed by the polar curve $r = 6 \cos \theta + 8 \sin \theta$ from $\theta = 0$ to $\theta = \pi$ is

(A) 28.274   (B) 50.265   (C) 78.540   (D) 113.097

Answer

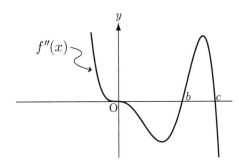

Note: This is the graph of $f''(x)$, NOT the graph of $f(x)$.

38. The figure above shows the graph of $f''(x)$, the second derivative of a function $f(x)$. The function $f(x)$ is continuous for all x. Which of the following statements about f are true?

    I. f is concave up for $x < 0$ and $b < x < c$.

    II. f has a relative minimum in the open interval $b < x < c$.

    III. f has points of inflection at $x = 0$ and $x = b$.

(A) I only

(B) II only

(C) III only

(D) I and III only

Answer

39. Let f be the function given by, $f(x) = \int_{0.1}^{x} \sin\left(\frac{1}{t}\right) dt$, $0.1 < x < 0.4$. At which of the following values of x does f have a relative maximum value?

(A) 0.106 only

(B) 0.159 only

(C) 0.318 only

(D) 0.106 and 0.318

Answer

40. Let $T(x) = \sum_{k=0}^{\infty} \left(\frac{1}{2}\right)^{k} \frac{(x-3)^{k}}{k!}$ be the Taylor series for a function f.

What is the value of $f^{(10)}(3)$, the tenth derivative of f at $x = 3$?

(A) 5.382×10^{-10}

(B) 2.691×10^{-10}

(C) 9.766×10^{-4}

(D) 4.883×10^{-4}

Answer

41. $\dfrac{d}{dx} \displaystyle\int_0^{2x} (e^t + 2t)\, dt =$

(A) $e^{2x} + 4x$

(B) $e^{2x} + 4x - 1$

(C) $2e^{2x} + 4x$

(D) $2e^{2x} + 8x$

Answer

42. On the interval $[0, b]$ the number $c = 4.522$ is the number guaranteed by the Mean Value Theorem for the function $f(x) = \sin(x)$. What is the approximate value of b ?

(A) 5.026   (B) 5.013   (C) 4.522   (D) 4.000

Answer

43. What is the approximate value of $\cos\left(\frac{1}{2}\right)$ obtained by using a fourth-degree Taylor polynomial for $\cos x$ about $x = 0$?

(A) $\frac{1}{2} - \frac{1}{24} + \frac{1}{640}$

(B) $1 - \frac{1}{4} + \frac{1}{16}$

(C) $1 - \frac{1}{8} + \frac{1}{64}$

(D) $1 - \frac{1}{8} + \frac{1}{384}$

Answer

44. If $\displaystyle\int_0^{1000} 8^x\, dx - \int_a^{1000} 8^x\, dx = 10.40$, then $a =$

(A) 1.4   (B) 1.5   (C) 1.6   (D) 1.7

Answer

45. If n is a positive integer, then $\displaystyle\lim_{n \to \infty} \frac{1}{n}\left[\frac{1}{1+(1/n)} + \frac{1}{1+(2/n)} + \cdots + \frac{1}{1+(n/n)}\right]$ can be expressed as

(A) $\displaystyle\int_0^1 \frac{1}{x}\,dx$

(B) $\displaystyle\int_1^2 \frac{1}{x+1}\,dx$

(C) $\displaystyle\int_1^2 \frac{2}{x+1}\,dx$

(D) $\displaystyle\int_1^2 \frac{1}{x}\,dx$

Answer

FREE-RESPONSE QUESTIONS — GENERAL INSTRUCTIONS

For each part of Section II, you may wish to look over the problems before starting to work on them. It is not expected that everyone will be able to complete all parts of all problems. All problems are given equal weight, but the parts of a particular problem are not necessarily given equal weight.

YOU SHOULD WRITE ALL WORK FOR EACH PART OF EACH PROBLEM IN THE SPACE PROVIDED FOR THAT PART. Be sure to write clearly and legibly. If you make an error, you may save time by crossing it out rather than trying to erase it. Erased or crossed-out work will not be graded. Manage your time carefully.

- Show all your work, even though a question may not explicitly remind you to do so. Clearly label any functions, graphs, tables, or other objects that you use. Your work will be graded on the correctness and completeness of your methods as well as your answers. Answers without supporting work will usually not receive credit.

- Justifications require that you give mathematical (noncalculator) reasons.

- Your work must be expressed in standard mathematical notation rather than calculator syntax. For example, $\int_1^5 x^2\,dx$ may not be written as fnInt(X^2, X, 1, 5).

- Unless otherwise specified, answers (numeric or algebraic) need not be simplified.

- If you use decimal approximations in calculations, your work will be graded on accuracy. Unless otherwise specified, your final answers should be accurate to three places after the decimal point.

- Unless otherwise specified, the domain of a function f is assumed to be the set of all real numbers x for which $f(x)$ is a real number.

SECTION II PART A: 30 Minutes, Questions 1,2

A graphing calculator is required.

During the timed portion for Part A, you may work only on the problems in Part A. Write your solution to each part of each problem in the space provided.

On Part A, you are permitted to use your calculator to solve an equation, find the derivative of a function at a point, or calculate the value of a definite integral. However, you must clearly indicate the setup of your programs, you must show the mathematical steps necessary to produce your results.

Do not go on to Part B until you are told to do so.

SECTION II PART B: 60 Minutes, Questions 3,4,5,6

Write your solution to each part of each problem in the space provided for that part. During the timed portion for Part B, you may continue to work on the problems in Part A without the use of any calculator.

Section II Part A: A graphing calculator is required for these problems.

1. Two particles move in the *xy*-plane. Particle A moves along the graph of $y = 1 + e^{-x}$ and particle B moves along the graph $y = \cos x$ for $0 \le x \le 3\pi$. At all times their *x*-coordinates are the same.

   (a) Sketch the graph of the paths of the particles on the axes provided.

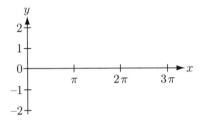

   (b) Will the particles ever collide? Justify your answer.

   (c) What is the minimum vertical distance between the particles? Show the computations that lead to your answer.

   (d) What is the maximum vertical distance between the particles? Show the computations that lead to your answer.

   (a) Sketch the graph of the paths of the particles on the axes provided.

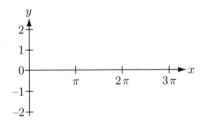

(b) Will the particles ever collide? Justify your answer.

(c) What is the minimum vertical distance between the particles? Show the computations that lead to your answer.

(d) What is the maximum vertical distance between the particles? Show the computations that lead to your answer.

2. The amount of radiation, $R(t)$, in a certain liquid decreases at a rate proportional to the amount present, that is, $\frac{dR}{dt} = kR$, where k is a constant and t is measured in seconds. The initial amount of radiation is 10^6 rads. After 100 seconds the radiation has dropped to 10^2 rads.

(a) Express R as a function of t.

(b) To the nearest second, when will the amount of radiation drop below 10 rads?

(c) What is the half-life of this chemical–that is, how long does it take for the amount of radiation to reach half of the original amount?

(a) Express R as a function of t.

(b) To the nearest second, when will the amount of radiation drop below 10 rads?

(c) What is the half-life of this chemical–that is, how long does it take for the amount of radiation to reach half of the original amount?

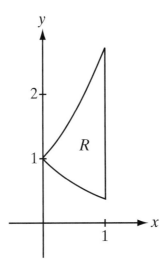

3. Let R be the region bounded by the graphs of $y = e^x$, $y = e^{-x}$ and the vertical line $x = 1$, as shown in the figure above.

(a)   Find the area of R.

(b)   Find the volume of the solid generated when R is revolved around the x-axis.

(c)   The region R is the base of a solid. For each x, $0 \le x \le 1$, the cross sections perpendicular to the x-axis will be rectangles. The base of these rectangles lies in region R and the heights of the rectangles are equal to the x-coordinates of the cross sections. Write, but do not evaluate, an integral expression that gives the volume of the solid.

(a)   Find the area of R.

(b) Find the volume of the solid generated when R is revolved around the x-axis.

(c) The region R is the base of a solid. For each x, $0 \leq x \leq 1$, the cross sections perpendicular to the x-axis will be rectangles. The base of these rectangles lies in region R and the heights of the rectangles are equal to the x-coordinates of the cross sections. Write, but do not evaluate, an integral expression that gives the volume of the solid.

4. A particle is moving in the xy-plane so that for all t :

$$\frac{dx}{dt} = 4\cos t \text{ and } \frac{dy}{dt} = \sin t$$

At $t = 0$, the particle is at the origin.

(a)   Find $x(t)$ and $y(t)$, the parametric equations for the position of the particle.

(b)   Find the average rate of change of y with respect to x as t varies from 0 to $\frac{\pi}{2}$.

(c)   At what time t, $0 \le t \le \frac{\pi}{2}$, will the instantaneous rate of change of y with respect to x be equal to the average rate of change of y with respect to x ?

(a)   Find $x(t)$ and $y(t)$, the parametric equations for the position of the particle.

(b)   Find the average rate of change of y with respect to x as t varies from 0 to $\frac{\pi}{2}$.

(c)   At what time t, $0 \le t \le \frac{\pi}{2}$, will the instantaneous rate of change of y with respect to x be equal to the average rate of change of y with respect to x ?

5. The fifth-degree Maclaurin polynomial for $\tan(x)$ is $M(x) = x + \frac{1}{3}x^3 + \frac{2}{15}x^5$.

   (a)   Use $M(x)$ to find the 4th degree Maclaurin polynomial for $\sec^2(x)$.

   (b)   Use $M(x)$ to find the 4th degree Maclaurin polynomial for $\frac{\tan(x)}{x}$.

   (c)   Use the polynomial found in (b) to find $\displaystyle\lim_{x \to 0} \frac{\tan(x)}{x}$.

   (d)   Is the limit found in (c) exact or an approximation? Explain your reasoning.

   (a)   Use $M(x)$ to find the 4th degree Maclaurin polynomial for $\sec^2(x)$.

   (b)   Use $M(x)$ to find the 4th degree Maclaurin polynomial for $\frac{\tan(x)}{x}$.

(c) Use the polynomial found in (b) to find $\lim\limits_{x \to 0} \dfrac{\tan(x)}{x}$.

(d) Is the limit found in (c) exact or an approximation? Explain your reasoning.

6. Consider the differential equation $y + \dfrac{dy}{dx} = e^{-x}$

   (a)   The slope field for the differential equation is provided. Sketch the solution curve that passes through $(0,0)$, and sketch the solution curve that passes through $(-2,0)$.

   (b)   For any constant C verify that $y = xe^{-x} + Ce^{-x}$ is a solution to the given differential equation.

   (c)   Each solution curve has a maximum value and no minimum value. In terms of C find the coordinates of the point where the maximum value occurs and find a function, $f(x)$, on which all the maximum points lie. Show the work that leads to your answer.

   (a)   The slope field for the differential equation is provided. Sketch the solution curve that passes through $(0,0)$, and sketch the solution curve that passes through $(-2,0)$.

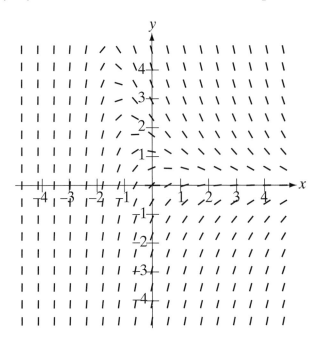

(b)   For any constant C verify that $y = xe^{-x} + Ce^{-x}$ is a solution to the given differential equation.

(c)   Each solution curve has a maximum value and no minimum value. In terms of C find the coordinates of the point where the maximum value occurs and find a function, $f(x)$, on which all the maximum points lie. Show the work that leads to your answer.

NO TESTING MATERIAL ON THIS PAGE

FORMULAS AND THEOREMS
FOR REFERENCE

I. Trigonometric Formulas

1. $\sin^2\theta + \cos^2\theta = 1$

2. $1 + \tan^2\theta = \sec^2\theta$

3. $1 + \cot^2\theta = \csc^2\theta$

4. $\sin(-\theta) = -\sin\theta$

5. $\cos(-\theta) = \cos\theta$

6. $\tan(-\theta) = -\tan\theta$

7. $\sin(A+B) = \sin A \cos B + \sin B \cos A$

8. $\sin(A-B) = \sin A \cos B - \sin B \cos A$

9. $\cos(A+B) = \cos A \cos B - \sin A \sin B$

10. $\cos(A-B) = \cos A \cos B + \sin A \sin B$

11. $\sin 2\theta = 2\sin\theta\cos\theta$

12. $\cos 2\theta = \cos^2\theta - \sin^2\theta = 2\cos^2\theta - 1 = 1 - 2\sin^2\theta$

13. $\tan\theta = \dfrac{\sin\theta}{\cos\theta} = \dfrac{1}{\cot\theta}$

14. $\cot\theta = \dfrac{\cos\theta}{\sin\theta} = \dfrac{1}{\tan\theta}$

15. $\sec\theta = \dfrac{1}{\cos\theta}$

16. $\csc\theta = \dfrac{1}{\sin\theta}$

17. $\cos\left(\dfrac{\pi}{2} - \theta\right) = \sin\theta$

18. $\sin\left(\dfrac{\pi}{2} - \theta\right) = \cos\theta$

II. Differentiation Formulas

1. $\dfrac{d}{dx}(x^n) = nx^{n-1}$

2. $\dfrac{d}{dx}(fg) = fg' + gf'$

3. $\dfrac{d}{dx}\left(\dfrac{f}{g}\right) = \dfrac{gf' - fg'}{g^2}$

4. $\dfrac{d}{dx}(f(g(x))) = f'(g(x))\, g'(x)$

5. $\dfrac{d}{dx}(\sin x) = \cos x$

6. $\dfrac{d}{dx}(\cos x) = -\sin x$

7. $\dfrac{d}{dx}(\tan x) = \sec^2 x$

8. $\dfrac{d}{dx}(\cot x) = -\csc^2 x$

9. $\dfrac{d}{dx}(\sec x) = \sec x \tan x$

10. $\dfrac{d}{dx}(\csc x) = -\csc x \cot x$

11. $\dfrac{d}{dx}(e^x) = e^x$

12. $\dfrac{d}{dx}(a^x) = a^x \ln a,\ a > 0,\ a \neq 1$

13. $\dfrac{d}{dx}(\ln x) = \dfrac{1}{x}$

14. $\dfrac{d}{dx}(\sin^{-1}x) = \dfrac{1}{\sqrt{1 - x^2}}$

15. $\dfrac{d}{dx}(\tan^{-1}x) = \dfrac{1}{1 + x^2}$

16. $\dfrac{d}{dx}(\cos^{-1}x) = \dfrac{-1}{\sqrt{1 - x^2}}$

III. Integration Formulas

1. $\displaystyle\int a\,dx = ax + C$

2. $\displaystyle\int \frac{1}{x}\,dx = \ln|x| + C$

3. $\displaystyle\int e^x\,dx = e^x + C$

4. $\displaystyle\int a^x\,dx = \frac{a^x}{\ln a} + C$

5. $\displaystyle\int x^n\,dx = \frac{x^{n+1}}{n+1} + C, n \neq -1$

6. $\displaystyle\int \sin x\,dx = -\cos x + C$

7. $\displaystyle\int \cos x\,dx = \sin x + C$

8. $\displaystyle\int \tan x\,dx = \ln|\sec x| + C \text{ or } -\ln|\cos x| + C$

9. $\displaystyle\int \cot x\,dx = \ln|\sin x| + C$

10. $\displaystyle\int \sec x\,dx = \ln|\sec x + \tan x| + C$

11. $\displaystyle\int \csc x\,dx = \ln|\csc x - \cot x| + C$

12. $\displaystyle\int \sec^2 x\,dx = \tan x + C$

13. $\displaystyle\int \sec x \tan x\,dx = \sec x + C$

14. $\displaystyle\int \csc^2 x\,dx = -\cot x + C$

15. $\displaystyle\int \csc x \cot x\,dx = -\csc x + C$

16. $\displaystyle\int \tan^2 x\,dx = \tan x - x + C$

17. $\displaystyle\int \frac{dx}{a^2 + x^2} = \frac{1}{a}\tan^{-1}\left(\frac{x}{a}\right) + C$

18. $\displaystyle\int \frac{dx}{\sqrt{a^2 - x^2}} = \sin^{-1}\left(\frac{x}{a}\right) + C$

IV. Formulas and Theorems

1. Limits and Continuity

A function $y = f(x)$ is continuous at $x = a$ if:

    i) $f(a)$ is defined (exists)

    ii) $\lim\limits_{x \to a} f(x)$ exists, and

    iii) $\lim\limits_{x \to a} f(x) = f(a)$

Otherwise, f is discontinuous at $x = a$.

$\lim\limits_{x \to a} f(x)$ exists if and only if both corresponding one-sided limits exist and are equal — that is,

$$\lim_{x \to a} f(x) = L \iff \lim_{x \to a^+} f(x) = L = \lim_{x \to a^-} f(x)$$

2. L'Hospital's Rule

If $\lim\limits_{x \to a} \dfrac{f(x)}{g(x)}$ is of the form $\dfrac{0}{0}$ or $\dfrac{\infty}{\infty}$, and if $\lim\limits_{x \to a} \dfrac{f'(x)}{g'(x)}$ exists, then $\lim\limits_{x \to a} \dfrac{f(x)}{g(x)} = \lim\limits_{x \to a} \dfrac{f'(x)}{g'(x)}$.

3. Limits of Rational Functions as $x \to \pm\infty$

    1. $\lim\limits_{x \to \pm\infty} \dfrac{f(x)}{g(x)} = 0$ if the degree of $f(x) <$ the degree of $g(x)$

    2. $\lim\limits_{x \to \pm\infty} \dfrac{f(x)}{g(x)}$ is infinite if the degree of $f(x) >$ the degree of $g(x)$

    3. $\lim\limits_{x \to \pm\infty} \dfrac{f(x)}{g(x)}$ is finite if the degree of $f(x) =$ the degree of $g(x)$

    Note: The limit will be the ratio of the leading coefficient of $f(x)$ to that of $g(x)$.

4. Intermediate Value Theorem

A function $y = f(x)$ that is continuous on a closed interval $[a,b]$ takes on every value between $f(a)$ and $f(b)$.

Note: If f is continuous on $[a,b]$ and $f(a)$ and $f(b)$ differ in sign, then the equation $f(x) = 0$ has at least one solution in the open interval (a,b).

5. Horizontal and Vertical Asymptotes

1. A line $y = b$ is a horizontal asymptote of the graph of $y = f(x)$ if either $\lim\limits_{x \to +\infty} f(x) = b$ or $\lim\limits_{x \to -\infty} f(x) = b$.

2. A line $x = a$ is a vertical asymptote of the graph of $y = f(x)$ if either $\lim\limits_{x \to a^+} f(x) = \pm\infty$ or $\lim\limits_{x \to a^-} f(x) = \pm\infty$.

6. Rates of Change

1. <u>Average Rate of Change</u>: If (x_0, y_0) and (x_1, y_1) are points on the graph of $y = f(x)$, then the average rate of change of y with respect to x over the interval $[x_0, x_1]$ is
$$\frac{f(x_1) - f(x_0)}{x_1 - x_0} = \frac{y_1 - y_0}{x_1 - x_0} = \frac{\Delta y}{\Delta x}.$$

2. <u>Instantaneous Rate of Change</u>: If (x_0, y_0) is a point on the graph of $y = f(x)$, then the instantaneous rate of change of y with respect to x at x_0 is $f'(x_0)$.

7. Definition of the Derivative

$$f'(x) = \lim\limits_{h \to 0} \frac{f(x + h) - f(x)}{h} \quad \text{or} \quad f'(a) = \lim\limits_{x \to a} \frac{f(x) - f(a)}{x - a}$$

The latter definition of the derivative is the instantaneous rate of change of $f(x)$ with respect to x at $x = a$.

Geometrically, the derivative of a function at a point is the slope of the tangent line to the graph of the function at that point.

8. The number e

1. $\lim\limits_{n \to +\infty} \left(1 + \frac{1}{n}\right)^n = e$

2. $\lim\limits_{n \to 0} (1 + n)^{\frac{1}{n}} = e$

3. $\sum\limits_{n=0}^{\infty} \frac{1}{n!} = e$

9. Rolle's Theorem

If f is continuous on $[a,b]$ and differentiable on (a,b) such that $f(a) = f(b)$, then there is at least one number c in the open interval (a,b) such that $f'(c) = 0$.

10. Mean Value Theorem

If f is continuous on $[a,b]$ and differentiable on (a,b), then there is at least one number c in (a,b) such that $\dfrac{f(b) - f(a)}{b - a} = f'(c)$.

11. Let f be differentiable for $a < x < b$ and continuous for $a \leq x \leq b$.

1. If $f'(x) > 0$ for every x in (a,b), then f is increasing on $[a,b]$.
2. If $f'(x) < 0$ for every x in (a,b), then f is decreasing on $[a,b]$.

12. Suppose that $f''(x)$ exists on the interval (a,b).

1. If $f''(x) > 0$ in (a,b), then f is concave upward in (a,b).
2. If $f''(x) < 0$ in (a,b), then f is concave downward in (a,b).

To locate the points of inflection of $y = f(x)$, find the points where $f''(x) = 0$ or where $f''(x)$ fails to exist. These are the only candidates where $f(x)$ may have a point of inflection. Then test these points to make sure that $f''(x) < 0$ on one side and $f''(x) > 0$ on the other.

13. Extreme Value Theorem

If f is continuous on a closed interval $[a,b]$, then $f(x)$ has both a maximum and a minimum on $[a,b]$.

14. First Derivative Test for Maximum and Minimum Points

- Locate the critical points $x = c$ of the function $f(x)$, that is, where $f'(c) = 0$ or $f'(c)$ is undefined.
- Check any changes in signs of $f'(x)$ to the left and right of $x = c$.
- If $f'(x)$ changes from negative to positive then there exists a relative minimum at $x = c$.
- If $f'(x)$ changes from positive to negative then there exists a relative maximum at $x = c$.

Note: On a closed interval the endpoints must also be checked and compared to the values above so as to determine the absolute maximum and minimum points for $f(x)$.

15. Second Derivative Test for Maximum and Minimum Points

If $f(x)$ is a twice-differentiable function at a critical point c, such that $f'(c) = 0$, substitute the value of c into the second derivative. If the second derivative is positive at $x = c$, the function is concave up at that point and there is a relative minimum there. If the second derivative is negative at $x = c$, then the curve is concave down at that point and there is a relative maximum at $x = c$.

Note: If $f'(c)$ and $f''(c)$ are both equal to 0, the second derivative test fails.

16. Differentiability implies continuity: If a function is differentiable at a point $x = a$, it is continuous at that point. The converse is false, i.e., continuity does <u>not</u> imply differentiability.

17. Local Linearity and Linear Approximation

The linear approximation of $f(x)$ near $x = x_0$ is given by $y = f(x_0) + f'(x_0)(x - x_0)$.

18. Inverse Functions

1. If f and g are two functions such that $f(g(x)) = x$ for every x in the domain of g, and, $g(f(x)) = x$, for every x in the domain of f, then, f and g are inverse functions of each other.
2. A function f has an inverse function if and only if no horizontal line intersects its graph more than once.
3. If f is either increasing or decreasing in an interval, then f has an inverse function over that interval.
4. If f is differentiable at every point on an interval I, and $f'(x) \neq 0$ on I, then $g = f^{-1}(x)$ is differentiable at every point of the interior of the interval $f(\mathrm{I})$ and $g'(f(x)) = \dfrac{1}{f'(x)}$.

19. Properties of e^x

1. The exponential function $y = e^x$ is the inverse function of $y = \ln x$.

2. The domain is the set of all real numbers, $-\infty < x < \infty$.

3. The range is the set of all positive numbers, $y > 0$.

4. $\dfrac{d}{dx}(e^x) = e^x$.

5. $y = e^x$ is continuous, increasing, and concave up for all x.

6. $\lim\limits_{x \to +\infty} e^x = +\infty$ and $\lim\limits_{x \to -\infty} e^x = 0$.

7. $e^{\ln x} = x$, for $x > 0$; $\ln(e^x) = x$ for all x.

20. Properties of $\ln x$

1. The domain of $y = \ln x$ is the set of all positive numbers, $x > 0$.

2. The range of $y = \ln x$ is the set of all real numbers, $-\infty < y < \infty$.

3. $y = \ln x$ is continuous, increasing, and concave down everywhere on its domain.

4. $\ln(ab) = \ln a + \ln b$; $\ln(a/b) = \ln a - \ln b$; $\ln a^r = r \ln a$

5. $y = \ln x < 0$ if $0 < x < 1$ and $\ln x > 0$ if $x > 1$; $\ln 1 = 0$; $\ln e = 1$.

6. $\lim\limits_{x \to +\infty} \ln x = +\infty$ and $\lim\limits_{x \to 0^+} \ln x = -\infty$.

7. $\log_a x = \dfrac{\ln x}{\ln a}$

21. Properties of the Definite Integral

Let $f(x)$ and $g(x)$ be continuous on $[a,b]$.

1. $\displaystyle\int_a^b c \cdot f(x)\, dx = c \int_a^b f(x)\, dx$, c is a nonzero constant.

2. $\displaystyle\int_a^a f(x)\, dx = 0$

3. $\displaystyle\int_b^a f(x)\, dx = -\int_a^b f(x)\, dx$

4. $\displaystyle\int_a^b f(x)\, dx = \int_a^c f(x)\, dx + \int_c^b f(x)\, dx$, where f is continuous on an interval containing the numbers a, b, and c, regardless of the order of a, b, and c.

5. If $f(x)$ is an odd function, then $\displaystyle\int_{-a}^a f(x)\, dx = 0$

6. If $f(x)$ is an even function, then $\displaystyle\int_{-a}^a f(x)\, dx = 2\int_0^a f(x)\, dx$

7. If $f(x) \geq 0$ on $[a,b]$, then $\displaystyle\int_a^b f(x)\, dx \geq 0$

8. If $g(x) \geq f(x)$ on $[a,b]$, then $\displaystyle\int_a^b g(x)\, dx \geq \int_a^b f(x)\, dx$

22. Linear Velocity, Speed, and Acceleration

1. The <u>velocity</u> of an object tells how fast it is going <u>and</u> in which direction. Velocity is an instantaneous rate of change.

2. The <u>speed</u> of an object is the absolute value of the velocity, $|v(t)|$. The speed tells how fast the object is going disregarding its direction.

   The speed of a particle <u>increases</u> (speeds up) when the velocity and acceleration have the same signs. The speed <u>decreases</u> (slows down) when the velocity and acceleration have opposite signs.

3. The <u>acceleration</u> is the instantaneous rate of change of velocity – it is the derivative of the velocity – that is, $a(t) = v'(t)$. Negative acceleration (deceleration) means that the velocity is decreasing. The acceleration gives the rate at which the velocity is changing.

Therefore, if x is the displacement of a moving object and t is time, then:

i) $\text{velocity} = v(t) = x'(t) = \dfrac{dx}{dt}$

ii) $\text{acceleration} = a(t) = x''(t) = v'(t) = \dfrac{dv}{dt} = \dfrac{d^2x}{dt^2}$

iii) $v(t) = \displaystyle\int a(t)\, dt$

iv) $x(t) = \displaystyle\int v(t)\, dt$

v) $\text{total distance} = \displaystyle\int_{t_1}^{t_2} |v(t)|\, dt$

<u>Note</u>: The <u>average</u> velocity of a particle over the time interval from t_0 to another time t, is

$$\text{Average Velocity} = \frac{\text{change of position}}{\text{change in time}} = \frac{s(t) - s(t_0)}{t - t_0},$$ where $s(t)$ is the position of the particle at time t.

23. <u>Definition of the Definite Integral as the Limit of a Riemann Sum</u>

Suppose that a function $f(x)$ is continuous on the closed interval $[a,b]$. Divide the interval into n equal subintervals, of length $\Delta x = \dfrac{b-a}{n}$. Choose one number in each subinterval i.e. x_1 in the first, x_2 in the second, ...,x_k in the kth, ..., and x_n in the nth. Then $\displaystyle\lim_{n \to \infty} \sum_{k=1}^{n} f(x_k)\,\Delta x = \int_a^b f(x)\,dx$.

24. <u>Fundamental Theorem of Calculus</u>

1. $\displaystyle\int_a^b f(x)\,dx = F(b) - F(a)$, where $F'(x) = f(x)$.

2. $\dfrac{d}{dx}\displaystyle\int_a^x f(t)\,dt = f(x)$ and $\dfrac{d}{dx}\displaystyle\int_a^{g(x)} f(t)\,dt = f(g(x))\,g'(x)$.

25. The average (mean) value of $f(x)$ on $[a,b]$ is $\dfrac{1}{b-a}\displaystyle\int_a^b f(x)\,dx$.

26. <u>Area Between Curves</u>

If f and g are continuous functions such that $f(x) \geq g(x)$ on $[a,b]$, then the area between the curves is $\displaystyle\int_a^b [f(x) - g(x)]\,dx$.

27. <u>Integration By Parts</u>

If $u = f(x)$ and $v = g(x)$ and if $f'(x)$ and $g'(x)$ are continuous, then $\displaystyle\int u\,dv = uv - \int v\,du$.

<u>Note</u>: The goal of the procedure is to choose u and dv so that $\displaystyle\int v\,du$ is easier to integrate than the original problem.

<u>Suggestion</u>: When "choosing" u, remember the acronym L.I.A.T.E., where L is the logarithmic function, I is an inverse trigonometric function, A is an algebraic function, T is a trigonometric function, and E is the exponential function. Just choose u as the first expression in L.I.A.T.E. (and dv will be the remaining part of the integrand). For example, when integrating $\displaystyle\int x \ln x\,dx$, choose $u = \ln x$, since L comes first in L.I.A.T.E., and $dv = x\,dx$. When integrating $\displaystyle\int xe^x\,dx$, choose $u = x$, since x is an algebraic function, and A comes before E in L.I.A.T.E., and $dv = e^x\,dx$. One more example, when integrating $\displaystyle\int x \tan^{-1} x\,dx$, let $u = \text{Arctan } x$, since I comes before A in L.I.A.T.E., and $dv = x\,dx$.

28. Volume of Solids of Revolution

Lct f be nonnegative and continuous on $[a,b]$, and let R be the region bounded above by $y = f(x)$, below by the x-axis, and on the sides by the lines $x = a$ and $x = b$.

When this region R is revolved about the x-axis, it generates a solid (having circular cross sections) whose volume $V = \int_a^b \pi [f(x)]^2 dx$.

29. Volumes of Solids with Known Cross Sections

1. For cross sections of area $A(x)$, taken perpendicular to the x-axis, the volume of the solid equals $\int_a^b A(x)\, dx$.

2. For cross sections of area $A(y)$, taken perpendicular to the y-axis, the volume of the solid equals $\int_c^d A(y)\, dy$.

30. Solving Differential Equations: Graphically and Numerically

1. Slope Fields:

    At every point (x,y) a differential equation of the form $\frac{dy}{dx} = f(x,y)$ gives the slope of the member of the family of solutions that contains that point. A slope field is a graphical representation of this family of curves. At certain points in the plane, a short segment is drawn whose slope is equal to the value of the derivative at that point. These segments are tangent to the solution's graph at the given points.

    The slope field allows you to sketch the graph of the solution curve even though you do not have its equation. This is done by starting at any point (usually the point given by the initial condition), and moving from one point to the next in the direction indicated by the segments of the slope field.

    Some calculators have built in operations for drawing slope fields; for calculators without this feature there are programs available for drawing them.

2. Euler's Method:

    Euler's Method is a way of approximating points on the solution of a differential equation $\frac{dy}{dx} = f(x,y)$. The calculation uses the tangent line approximation to calculate the approximate coordinates of the points of the solution function. Starting with the given point the initial condition, (x_1, y_1), and a small step size, Δx, use the formulas $x_{n+1} = x_n + \Delta x$ and $y_{n+1} = y_n + f'(x_n, y_n)\Delta x$ to calculate succeeding points. The accuracy of the method decreases with larger values of Δx. The error increases as each successive point is used to find the next. Calculator programs are available for doing this calculation.

31. <u>Solving Differential Equations by Separating the Variables</u>

There are many techniques for solving differential equations. However, any differential equation you may be asked to solve on the BC Calculus Exam can be solved by separating the variables. Rewrite the equation as an equivalent equation with all the x and dx terms on one side and all the y and dy terms on the other. Antidifferentiate both sides to obtain an equation without dx or dy, but with one constant of integration. Use the initial condition to evaluate this constant.

32. <u>Definition of Arc Length</u>

If a differentiable function given by $y = f(x)$ represents a curve on the closed interval $[a,b]$, then the arc length of f between a and b is given by $s = \int_a^b \sqrt{1 + [f'(x)]^2} \, dx$.

33. <u>Improper Integral</u>

$\int_a^b f(x) \, dx$ is an improper integral if

1. f becomes infinite at one or more points in the interval of integration, or

2. one or both of the limits of integration is infinite, or

3. a combination of (1) and (2)

34. Parametric Form of the Derivative

If a smooth curve C is given by the parametric equations $x = f(t)$ and $y = g(t)$, then the slope of the curve C at (x,y) is $\dfrac{dy}{dx} = \dfrac{dy}{dt} \div \dfrac{dx}{dt}, \dfrac{dx}{dt} \neq 0.$

<u>Note:</u> The second derivative, $\dfrac{d^2 y}{dx^2} = \dfrac{d}{dx}\left[\dfrac{dy}{dx}\right] = \dfrac{d}{dt}\left[\dfrac{dy}{dx}\right] \div \dfrac{dx}{dt}.$

35. Arc Length in Parametric Form

If a curve C is given by $x = f(t)$ and $y = g(t)$ and these functions have continuous first derivatives with respect to t for $a \leq t \leq b$, and if the point $P(x,y)$ traces the curve exactly once as t moves from $t = a$ to $t = b$, then the length of the curve is given by

$$s = \int_a^b \sqrt{\left(\frac{dx}{dt}\right)^2 + \left(\frac{dy}{dt}\right)^2}\, dt = \int_a^b \sqrt{[f'(t)]^2 + [g'(t)]^2}\, dt.$$

36. Polar Coordinates

1. <u>Cartesian *vs.* Polar Coordinates:</u> The polar coordinates (r,θ) are related to the Cartesian coordinates (x,y) as follows:

$$x = r\cos\theta \text{ and } y = r\sin\theta;$$
$$\tan\theta = \frac{y}{x} \text{ and } x^2 + y^2 = r^2$$

2. <u>Area in Polar Coordinates:</u> If f is continuous and nonnegative on the interval $[\alpha,\beta]$, then the area of the region bounded by the graph of $r = f(\theta)$ between the rays $\theta = \alpha$ and $\theta = \beta$ is given by

$$A = \frac{1}{2}\int_\alpha^\beta r^2\, d\theta = \frac{1}{2}\int_\alpha^\beta [f(\theta)]^2\, d\theta$$

37. Sequences and Series

1. If a sequence $\{a_n\}$ has a limit L, that is, $\lim\limits_{n\to\infty} a_n = L$, then the sequence is said to <u>converge</u> to L. If there is no limit, the sequence <u>diverges</u>. If the sequence $\{a_n\}$ converges, then its limit is unique. Keep in mind that $\lim\limits_{n\to\infty} \dfrac{\ln n}{n} = 0$; $\lim\limits_{n\to\infty} x^{\frac{1}{n}} = 1$; $\lim\limits_{n\to\infty} \sqrt[n]{n} = 1$; $\lim\limits_{n\to\infty} \dfrac{x^n}{n!} = 0$. These limits are useful and arise frequently.

2. The harmonic series $\sum\limits_{n=1}^{\infty} \dfrac{1}{n}$ diverges; the geometric series $\sum\limits_{n=0}^{\infty} ar^n$ converges to $\dfrac{a}{1-r}$ if $|r| < 1$ and diverges if $|r| \geq 1$ and $a \neq 0$.

3. The p-series $\sum\limits_{n=1}^{\infty} \dfrac{1}{n^p}$ converges if $p > 1$ and diverges if $p \leq 1$.

4. <u>Limit Comparison Test</u>: Let $\sum_{n=1}^{\infty} a_n$ and $\sum_{n=1}^{\infty} b_n$ be a series of nonnegative terms, with $a_n \neq 0$ for all sufficiently large n, and suppose that $\lim_{n \to \infty} \dfrac{b_n}{a_n} = c > 0$. Then the two series either both converge of both diverge.

   i) If $\lim_{n \to \infty} \dfrac{b_n}{a_n} = 0$ and $\sum_{n=1}^{\infty} a_n$ converges, then $\sum_{n=1}^{\infty} b_n$ also converges.

   ii) If $\lim_{n \to \infty} \dfrac{b_n}{a_n} \to \infty$ and $\sum_{n=1}^{\infty} a_n$ diverges, then $\sum_{n=1}^{\infty} b_n$ also diverges.

5. <u>Alternating Series</u>: Let $\sum_{n=1}^{\infty} a_n$ be a series such that

   i) the series is alternating

   ii) $|a_{n+1}| \leq |a_n|$ for all n or at least after a finite number of terms, and

   iii) $\lim_{n \to \infty} a_n = 0$

   Then the series converges.

   iv) If $\sum_{n=1}^{\infty} a_n$ satisfies the above criteria then the function error is less than a_{n+1} and has the same sign as the first omitted term. (The Alternating Series Error Bound Theorem).

6. <u>The nth-Term Test for Divergence</u>: If $\lim_{n \to \infty} a_n \neq 0$, then the series diverges.

   Note that the converse is *false*, that is, if $\lim_{n \to \infty} a_n = 0$, the series may or may not converge.

7. A series $\sum a_n$ is <u>absolutely convergent</u> if the series $\sum |a_n|$ converges. If $\sum a_n$ converges, but $\sum |a_n|$ does not converge, then the series is <u>conditionally convergent</u>. Keep in mind that if $\sum_{n=1}^{\infty} |a_n|$ converges, then $\sum_{n=1}^{\infty} a_n$ converges.

8. <u>Direct Comparison Test</u>: If $0 \leq a_n \leq b_n$ for all sufficiently large n, and $\sum_{n=1}^{\infty} b_n$ converges, then $\sum_{n=1}^{\infty} a_n$ converges. If $\sum_{n=1}^{\infty} a_n$ diverges, then $\sum_{n=1}^{\infty} b_n$ diverges.

9. <u>Integral Test</u>: Let $f(x)$ be a positive, continuous, and decreasing function on $[1, \infty)$, and $a_n = f(n)$. The series $\sum_{n=1}^{\infty} a_n$ and the improper integral $\int_1^{\infty} f(x)\, dx$ either both converge or both diverge.

10. <u>Ratio Test</u>: Let $\sum a_n$ be a series with nonzero terms.

i) If $\lim\limits_{n \to \infty} \left| \dfrac{a_{n+1}}{a_n} \right| < 1$, then the series converges absolutely.

ii) If $\lim\limits_{n \to \infty} \left| \dfrac{a_{n+1}}{a_n} \right| > 1$, then the series is divergent.

iii) If $\lim\limits_{n \to \infty} \left| \dfrac{a_{n+1}}{a_n} \right| = 1$, then the test is inconclusive (and another approach must be used).

11. <u>Power Series</u>: A power series is a series of the form

$$\sum_{n=0}^{\infty} c_n x^n = c_0 + c_1 x + c_2 x^2 + \cdots + c_n x^n + \cdots \text{ or}$$

$$\sum_{n=0}^{\infty} c_n (x-a)^n = c_0 + c_1 (x-a) + c_2 (x-a)^2 + \cdots + c_n (x-a)^n + \cdots$$

in which the center a and the coefficients $c_0, c_1, c_2, \dots, c_n, \dots$ are constants.

The set of all numbers x for which the power series converges is called the interval of convergence.

12. <u>Taylor Series</u>: Let f be a function with derivatives of all orders throughout some interval containing a as an interior point. Then the Taylor series generated by f at a is

$$\sum_{n=0}^{\infty} \frac{f^{(n)}(a)}{n!}(x-a)^n = f(a) + f'(a)(x-a) + \frac{f''(a)}{2!}(x-a)^2 + \cdots + \frac{f^{(n)}(a)}{n!}(x-a)^n + \cdots$$

The remaining terms after the term containing the nth derivative can be expressed as a remainder to Taylor's Theorem:

$$f(x) = \sum_{n=1}^{\infty} \frac{f^{(n)}}{n!}(x-a)^n + R_n(x) \text{ where } R_n(x) = \frac{f^{(n+1)}(c)}{(n+1)!}(x-a)^{n+1} \text{ for some number } c$$

between x and a. The number $R_n(x)$ is called the Lagrange Form of the remainder. $\left| R_n(x) \right|$ can be used to estimate the size of the error when the finite Taylor polynomial is used to approximate the series. The series will converge for all values of x for which the remainder approaches zero as $n \to \infty$.

Lagrange's form of the remainder: $R_n(x) = \dfrac{f^{(n+1)}(c)(x-a)^{n+1}}{(n+1)!}$, where $x < c < a$.

13. <u>Radius of Convergence</u>:
1. If a power series centered at $x = a$ converges when $|x - a| < R$ and diverges when $|x - a| > R$, then the value of R is called the radius of convergence.
2. If the power series converges only when $x = a$, the radius of convergence is zero.
3. If the power series converges for every x, then the radius of convergence is infinite.

14. <u>Frequently Used Series and their Interval of Convergence</u>

$$\frac{1}{1-x} = 1 + x + x^2 + \cdots + x^n + \cdots = \sum_{n=0}^{\infty} x^n, \ |x| < 1$$

$$\sin x = x - \frac{x^3}{3!} + \frac{x^5}{5!} - \cdots + (-1)^n \frac{x^{2n+1}}{(2n+1)!} + \cdots = \sum_{n=0}^{\infty} \frac{(-1)^n x^{2n+1}}{(2n+1)!}, \ |x| < \infty$$

$$\cos x = 1 - \frac{x^2}{2!} + \frac{x^4}{4!} - \cdots + \frac{(-1)^n x^{2n}}{(2n)!} + \cdots = \sum_{n=0}^{\infty} \frac{(-1)^n x^{2n}}{(2n)!}, \ |x| < \infty$$

$$e^x = 1 + x + \frac{x^2}{2!} + \frac{x^3}{3!} + \cdots + \frac{x^n}{n!} + \cdots = \sum_{n=0}^{\infty} \frac{x^n}{n!}, \ |x| < \infty$$

38. <u>Vectors</u>

Vectors represent quantities that have magnitude and direction. The notation for a vector is an ordered pair expression consisting of a horizontal and vertical component.

Position: $\langle x(t), y(t) \rangle$

Velocity: $\langle x'(t), y'(t) \rangle$

Acceleration: $\langle x''(t), y''(t) \rangle$

Speed: $\sqrt{(x'(t))^2 + (y'(t))^2}$

39. <u>Logistic Growth Model for Population P</u>

1. Logistic differential equation: $\dfrac{dP}{dt} = k\,P(M - P)$

2. Solution equation: $P = \dfrac{M}{1 + Ae^{-Mkt}}$ where M is the maximum growth amount, k is the logistic growth constant and A is a constant based on the initial condition given.

INDEX

(for Multiple-Choice Questions)

Roman numerals in boldface type are Sample Examination numbers, followed by question numbers for the topic.